Editor
Jennifer Overend Prior, M. Ed.

Editorial Project Manager
Lori Kamola, M.S. Ed.

Editor-in-Chief
Sharon Coan, M.S. Ed.

Cover Artist
Lesley Palmer

Art Coordinator
Denice Adorno

Imaging
Alfred Lau
James Edward Grace
Temo Parra

Product Manager
Phil Garcia

Publishers
Rachelle Cracchiolo, M.S. Ed.
Mary Dupuy Smith, M.S. Ed.

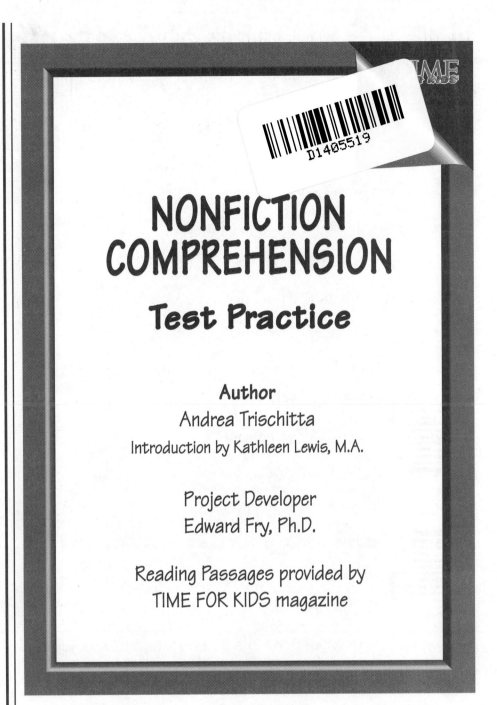

NONFICTION COMPREHENSION

Test Practice

Author
Andrea Trischitta

Introduction by Kathleen Lewis, M.A.

Project Developer
Edward Fry, Ph.D.

Reading Passages provided by
TIME FOR KIDS magazine

Teacher Created Materials, Inc.
6421 Industry Way
Westminster, CA 92683
www.teachercreated.com

ISBN-0-7439-3512-8

©2001 Teacher Created Materials, Inc.
Reprinted, 2005
Made in U.S.A.

Table of Contents

(**Note:** Each six-part lesson revolves around an article from *Time For Kids*. The article titles are listed here for you to choose topics that will appeal to your students, but the individual articles do not begin on the first page of the lessons. The lessons in this book may be done in any order.)

Introduction

Why Every Teacher Needs This Book

In a day of increased accountability and standards-based instruction, teachers are feeling greater pressure for their students to perform well on standardized tests. Every teacher knows that students who can read, and comprehend what they read, will have better test performance.

In many classrooms today, teachers experience challenges they are not trained to meet, including limited English speakers, students with disabilities, high student mobility rates, and student apathy. Many states with poor standardized test scores have students that come from print-poor environments. Teachers need help developing competent readers and students who can apply their knowledge in the standardized test setting.

The *Nonfiction Comprehension Test Practice* series is a tool that will help teachers to teach comprehension skills to their students and enable their students to perform better in a test setting. This series supplies motivating, readable, interesting, nonfiction text, and comprehension exercises to help students practice comprehension skills while truly becoming better readers. The activities can be quick or in depth, allowing students to practice skills daily. What is practiced daily will be acquired by students. Practice for standardized tests needs to be started at the beginning of the school year, not a few weeks before the tests. The articles in this series are current and develop knowledge about today's world as well as the past. Students will begin thinking, talking, and developing a framework of knowledge which is crucial for comprehension.

When a teacher sparks an interest in knowledge, students will become life-long learners. In the process of completing these test practice activities, not only will you improve your students' test scores, you will create better readers and life-long learners.

Readability

All of the articles used in this series have been edited for readability. The Fry Graph, The Dale-Chall Readability Formula, or the Spache Readability Formula was used depending on the level of the article. Of more than 100 predictive readability formulas, these are the most widely used. These formulas count and factor in three variables: the number of words, syllables, and sentences. The Dale-Chall and Spache formulas also use vocabulary lists. The Dale-Chall Formula is typically used for upper-elementary and secondary grade-level materials. It uses its own vocabulary list and takes into account the total number of words and sentences. The formula reliably gives the readability for the chosen text. The Spache Formula is vocabulary-based, paying close attention to the percentage of words not present in the formula's vocabulary list. This formula is best for evaluating primary and early elementary texts. Through the use of these formulas, the levels of the articles are appropriate and comprehensible for students at each grade level.

Introduction *(cont.)*

General Lesson Plan

At each grade level of this series, there are 20 articles that prove interesting and readable to students. Each article is followed by questions on the following topics:

Sentence comprehension—Five true/false statements are related back to one sentence from the text.

Word study—One word from the text is explained (origin, part of speech, unique meaning, etc.). Activities can include completion items (cloze statements), making illustrations, or compare and contrast items.

Paragraph comprehension—This section contains one paragraph from the text and five multiple-choice questions directly related to that paragraph. The questions range from drawing information directly from the page to forming opinions and using outside knowledge.

Whole story comprehension—Eight multiple-choice questions relate back to the whole article or a major part of it. They can include comprehension that is factual, is based on opinion, involves inference, uses background knowledge, involves sequencing or classifying, relates to cause and effect, and involves understanding the author's intent. All levels of reading comprehension are covered.

Enrichment for language mechanics and expression—This section develops language mechanics and expression through a variety of activities.

Graphic development—Graphic organizers that relate to the article are used to answer a variety of comprehension questions. In some lessons, students create their own maps, graphs, and diagrams that relate to the article.

The following is a list of words from the lessons that may be difficult for some students. These words are listed here so that you may review them with your students as needed.

Word	Page	Word	Page	Word	Page
coyote	20	carousel	55	uninhabited	103
ecological	21	prances	56	fjord	104
environmental	21	speleologist	63	Scandinavia	107
Giordano	25	aragonite	63	Kertesz	109
Messina	27	Ibis	75	aardvarks	110
Chaffinches	27	ecosystem	75	canine	114
Poachers	27	similes	77	premolar	114
ornithologist	27	canine distemper	79	Koorina	115
dishonorable	33	Serengeti	81	platypus	115
fertilized	37	wildebeests	81	Echidnas	119
bouquets	37	Endurance	87	Choctaw	123
Caribbean	44	acronym	101	extinct	123
meager	50	abbreviated	101	nutritionist	134

Introduction (cont.)

What Do Students Need to Learn?

Successful reading requires comprehension. Comprehending means having the ability to connect words and thoughts to knowledge already possessed. If you have little or no knowledge of a subject, it is difficult to comprehend an article or text written on that subject. Comprehension requires motivation and interest. Once your students start acquiring knowledge, they will want to fill in the gaps and learn more.

In order to help students be the best readers they can be, a teacher needs to be familiar with what students need to know to comprehend well. A teacher needs to know Bloom's levels of comprehension, traditional comprehension skills and expected products, and the types of questions that are generally used on standardized comprehension tests, as well as methods that can be used to help students to build a framework for comprehension.

Bloom's Taxonomy

In 1956, Benjamin Bloom created a classification for questions that are commonly used to demonstrate comprehension. These levels are listed here along with the corresponding skills that will demonstrate understanding and are important to remember when teaching comprehension to assure that students have attained higher levels of comprehension. Use this classification to form your own questions whenever students read or listen to literature.

Knowledge—Students will recall information. They will show knowledge of dates, events, places, and main ideas. Questions will include words such as: who, what, where, when, list, identify, and name.

Comprehension—Students will understand information. They will compare and contrast, order, categorize, and predict consequences. Questions will include words such as: compare, contrast, describe, summarize, predict, and estimate.

Application—Students will use information in new situations. Questions will include words such as: apply, demonstrate, solve, classify, and complete.

Analysis—Students will see patterns. They will be able to organize parts and figure out meaning. Questions will include words such as: order, explain, arrange, and analyze.

Synthesis—Students will use old ideas to create new ones. They will generalize, predict, and draw conclusions. Questions will include words such as: what if?, rewrite, rearrange, combine, create, and substitute.

Evaluation—Students will compare ideas and assess value. They will make choices and understand a subjective viewpoint. Questions will include words such as: assess, decide, and support your opinion.

Introduction (cont.)

Comprehension Skills

There are many skills that form the complex activity of comprehension. This wide range of understandings and abilities develops over time in competent readers. The following list includes many traditional skills found in scope and sequence charts and standards for reading comprehension.

identifies details

recognizes stated main idea

follows directions

determines sequence

recalls details

locates reference

recalls gist of story

labels parts

summarizes

recognizes anaphoric relationships

identifies time sequence

describes a character

retells story in own words

infers main idea

infers details

infers cause and effect

infers authors purpose/intent

classifies, places into categories

compares and contrasts

draws conclusions

makes generalizations

recognizes paragraph (text) organization

predicts outcome

recognizes hyperbole and exaggeration

experiences empathy for a character

experiences an emotional reaction to the text

judges quality/appeal of text

judges author's qualifications

recognizes facts vs. opinions

applies understanding to a new situation

recognizes literary style

recognizes figurative language

identifies mood

identifies plot and story line

Introduction *(cont.)*

Observable Comprehension Products

There are many exercises that students can complete when they comprehend the material they read. Some of these products can be performed orally in small groups. Some lend themselves more to independent paper-and-pencil type activities. Although there are more, the following are common and comprehensive products of comprehension.

Recognizing—underlining, multiple choice items, matching, true/false statements

Recalling—writing a short answer, filling in the blanks, flashcard question and answer

Paraphrasing—retelling in own words, summarizing

Classifying—grouping components, naming clusters, completing comparison tables, ordering components on a scale

Following directions—completing steps in a task, using a recipe, constructing

Visualizing—graphing, drawing a map, illustrating, making a time line, creating a flow chart

Fluent reading—accurate pronunciation, phrasing, intonation, dramatic qualities

Reading Comprehension Questions

Teaching the kinds of questions that appear on standardized tests gives students the framework to anticipate and thus look for the answers to questions while reading. This framework will not only help students' scores, but it will actually help them learn how to comprehend what they are reading. Some of the types of questions students will find on standardized comprehension tests are as follows:

Vocabulary—These questions are based on word meaning, common words, proper nouns, technical words, geographical words, and unusual adjectives.

Facts—These questions ask exactly what was written, using who, what, when, where, why, how, and how many.

Sequence—These questions are based on order—what happened first, last, and in between.

Conditionals—These questions use qualifying terms such as: if, could, alleged, etc.

Summarizing—These questions require students to restate, choose main ideas, conclude, and create a new title. Also important here is for students to understand and state the author's purpose.

Outcomes—These questions often involve readers drawing upon their own experiences or bringing outside knowledge to the composition. Students must understand cause and effect, results of actions, and implications.

Opinion—These questions ask the author's intent and mood and require use of background knowledge to answer.

Introduction (cont.)

Graphic Organizers

Reading and comprehension can be easier for students with a few simple practices. For top comprehension, students need a wide vocabulary, ideas about the subject they are reading, and understanding of the structure of the text. Pre-reading activities will help students in all of these areas. Graphic organizers help students build vocabulary, brainstorm ideas, and understand the structure of the text.

Graphic organizers aid students with vocabulary and comprehension. Graphic organizers can help students comprehend more and, in turn, gain insight into how to comprehend in future readings. This process teaches a student a way to connect new information to prior knowledge that is stored in his or her brain. Different types of graphic organizers are listed below by category.

Concept organizers include: semantic maps, spider maps (word webs), Venn diagrams, and fishbone diagrams.

Semantic map—This organizer builds vocabulary. A word for study is placed in the center of the page, and four categories are made around it. The categories expand on the nature of the word and relate it back to personal knowledge and experience of the students.

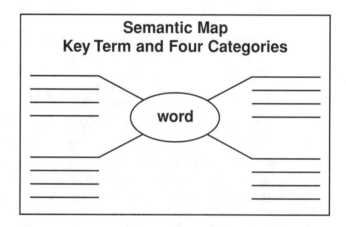

Spider map (word web)—The topic, concept, or theme is placed in the middle of the page. Like a spider's web, thoughts and ideas come out from the center, beginning with main ideas and flowing out to details.

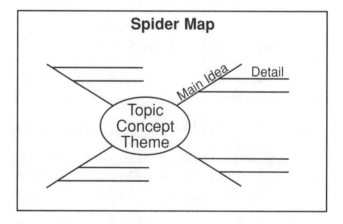

Introduction (cont.)

Venn diagram—This organizer compares and contrasts two ideas. With two large circles intersecting, each circle represents a different topic. The area of each circle that does not intersect is for ideas and concepts that are only true about one topic. The intersection is for ideas and concepts that are true about both topics.

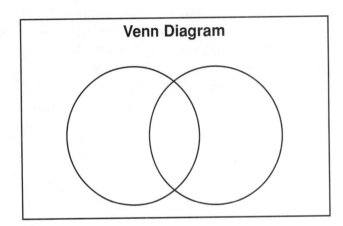

Fishbone diagram—This organizer deals with cause and effect. The result is listed first, branching out in a fishbone pattern with the causes that lead up to the result, along with other effects that happened along the way.

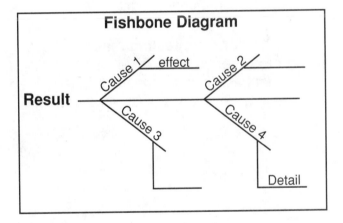

Continuum organizers can be linear or circular and contain a chain of events. These include time lines, chain of events, multiple linear maps, and circular or repeating maps.

Time lines—Whether graphing ancient history or the last hour, time lines help students to see how events have progressed and understand patterns in history.

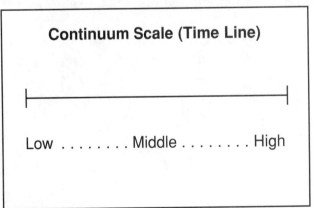

Introduction (cont.)

Graphic Organizers (cont.)

Chain of Events—This organizer not only shows the progression of time but also emphasizes cause and effect. Beginning with the initiating event inside of a box, subsequent arrows and boxes follow showing the events in order.

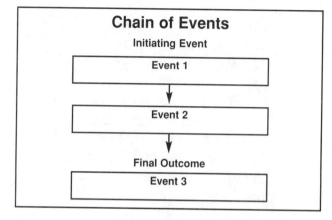

Multiple linear maps—These organizers can help students visualize how different events can be happening at the same time, either in history or in a story, and how those events affect each other.

Circular or repeating maps—These organizers lend themselves to events that happen in a repeating pattern like events in science, such as the water cycle.

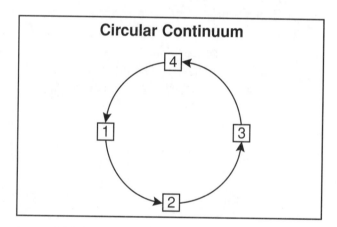

Hierarchical organizers show structure. These include: network trees, structured overviews, and class/example and properties maps. These organizers help students begin to visualize and comprehend hierarchy of knowledge, going from the big picture to the details.

Network tree—This organizer begins with a main, general topic. From there it branches out to examples of that topic, further branching out with more and more detail.

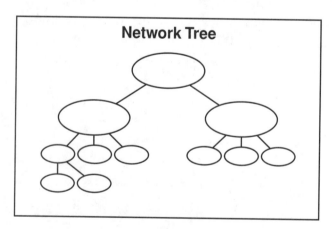

Introduction (cont.)

Structured overview—This is very similar to a network tree, but it varies in that it has a very structured look.

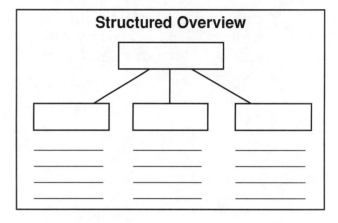

Class/example and properties map—Organized graphically, this map gives the information of class, example, and properties.

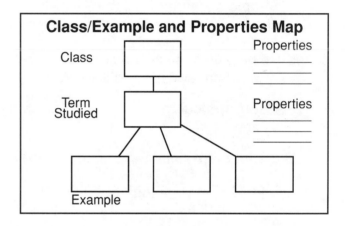

Spreadsheets are important organizers today. Much computer information is stored on spreadsheets. It is important for students to learn how to create, read, and comprehend these organizers. These include semantic feature analysis, compare and contrast matrices, and simple spreadsheet tables.

Semantic feature analysis—This organizer gives examples of a topic and lists features. A plus or a minus indicates if that example possesses those features.

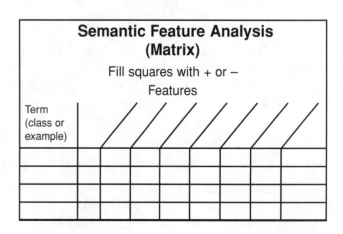

Introduction (cont.)

Graphic Organizers (cont.)

Compare and contrast matrix—This organizer compares and contrasts two or more examples on different attributes.

Compare/Contrast Matrix (Spreadsheets)		
Attribute 1		
Attribute 2		
Attribute 3		

Simple spreadsheet table—Much information can be visualized through spreadsheets or tables. Choose examples and qualities and arrange them in spreadsheet style.

Maps are helpful in understanding spatial relationships. There are geographical maps, but there are also street maps and floor plans.

Geographical map—These organizers can range from globes to cities and details are limited.

Street map—Information on this type of organizer becomes more detailed.

Floor plan—This organizer becomes more detailed, from a building to a room or a student's desk.

Numerical graphs such as bar graphs, pie charts, and tables become important in comprehension, too.

Bar graph—With a vertical and a horizontal axis, this graph shows a comparison between subjects. It is important to be able to draw the correct information out of it.

Pie chart—In the circular shape of a pie, amounts totaling 100% are shown as pieces of pie. Once again, drawing correct information is important.

Using graphic organizers while reading class material will help students know what to do in order to better comprehend material on standardized comprehension tests. Further, a varied use of all types of organizers will help students of different learning styles hit a method that works for them.

Pre-reading Strategies

It is widely understood that for comprehension and acquisition to take place, new information must be integrated with what the reader knows. Pre-reading strategies will help students to build knowledge and restructure the information they already possess in order to more fully comprehend what they are reading. After a teacher has spent time teaching pre-reading strategies, students will know what to do when reading on their own.

Introduction *(cont.)*

Building Vocabulary

Common sense reveals that there is a symbiotic relationship between knowledge of vocabulary and comprehension. Vocabulary development and comprehension span the curriculum. Students come across a large and diverse vocabulary in science, social science, mathematics, art, and even physical education. Skills and strategies for understanding vocabulary can be taught throughout the day. You can build your students' vocabulary directly and/or indirectly. Both ways have shown merit for different learners, so a combination will be sure to help all of the learners in your classroom.

Whether done directly or indirectly, teaching the kind of vocabulary that occurs in a text will greatly improve comprehension. Teaching vocabulary directly, a teacher would list the vocabulary in the text and have the students find the definitions in some manner. Indirectly, a teacher would introduce the content of the text and then elicit vocabulary that the students bring with them on the subject. The use of graphic organizers is helpful in doing this. (See page 8 for different types.) The teacher would lead the discussion to specific words if necessary.

> **Direct teaching**—The more conventional way of teaching vocabulary has its merits. Give students a list of vocabulary words and they look them up. This way teaches the use of reference materials and for some learners it is a good way to learn vocabulary. However, students truly learn vocabulary when they are involved in the construction of meaning rather than simply memorizing definitions.

> **Incidental or indirect teaching**—This is really a combination of direct teaching and incidental learning for the well-equipped teacher. Teaching in this fashion, a teacher uses the students' knowledge and interests to begin a vocabulary development session that will end with what he or she wants the students to learn. Along the way, the teacher builds a grand vocabulary list and student interest. Also, students buy into the fact that they are part of the process and that learning vocabulary can be a personal experience that they can control. The students will learn how to become independent learners, studying things that interest them.

A general approach to building vocabulary could include the following:

> **Semantic association**—Students brainstorm a list of words associated with a familiar word, sharing everyone's knowledge of vocabulary and discussing the less familiar words.

> **Semantic mapping**—Once the brainstorming is done, students can group the words into categories, creating a visual organization to understand relationships.

> **Semantic feature analysis**—Another way to group words is according to certain features. Use a chart to show similarities and differences between words.

> **Analogies**—This practice will further help students to see the relationships of words. Also, analogies are often used on standardized tests. (e.g., Doctor is to patient as teacher is to __*student*__ .)

> **Word roots and origins**—The study of these, as well as affixes, will help students to deduce new words. Students can ask themselves, "Does it look like a word I know? Can I figure out the meaning in the given context?"

Introduction *(cont.)*

═══════════ **Building Vocabulary** *(cont.)* ═══════════

Synonyms and antonyms—The study of these related words provides a structure for meaning and is also good practice for learning and building vocabulary.

Brainstorming—The use of graphic organizers to list and categorize ideas will help greatly with comprehension. A great way to get started is with a KWL chart. By listing ideas that are known, what students want to know, and, when finished, what they learned, relationships will be established so that comprehension and acquisition of knowledge will take place. Word webs work well, too. Anticipating the types of words and ideas that will appear in the text will help with fluency of reading as well as with comprehension.

═══════════ **Understanding Structure** ═══════════

To be able to make predictions and find information in writing, a student must understand structure. From the structure of a sentence to a paragraph to an essay, this skill is important and sometimes overlooked in instruction. Some students have been so immersed in literature that they have a natural understanding of structure. For instance, they know that a fairy tale starts out "Once upon a time . . . ," has a good guy and a bad guy, has a problem with a solution, and ends ". . . happily ever after." But when a student does not have this prior knowledge, making heads or tails of a fairy tale is difficult. The same holds true with not understanding that the first sentence of a paragraph will probably contain the main idea, followed with examples of that idea. When looking back at a piece to find the answer to a question, understanding structure will allow students to quickly scan the text for the correct area in which to find the information. Furthermore, knowing where a text is going to go structurally will help prediction as well as comprehension.

Building a large vocabulary is important for comprehension, but comprehension and acquisition also require a framework for relating new information to what is already in the brain. Students must be taught the structure of sentences and paragraphs. Knowing the structure of these, they will begin to anticipate and predict what will come next. Not having to decode every word reduces the time spent reading a sentence and thus helps students remember what they read at the beginning of the sentence. Assessing an author's purpose and quickly recalling a graphic or framework of personal knowledge will help a reader predict and anticipate what vocabulary and ideas might come up in an article or story.

Several activities will help with understanding structure. The following list offers some ideas to help students:

Write—A great way to understand structure is to use it. Teach students the proper structure when they write.

Color code—When reading a text, students can use colored pencils or crayons to color code certain elements such as main idea, supporting sentences, and details. Once the colors are in place, they can study and tell in their own words about paragraph structure.

Introduction *(cont.)*

Understanding Structure *(cont.)*

Go back in the text—Discuss a comprehension question with students. Ask them, "What kinds of words are you going to look for in the text to find the answer? Where are you going to look for them?" (The students should pick main ideas in the question and look for those words in the topic sentences of the different paragraphs.)

Graphic organizers—Use the list of graphic organizers (page 8) to find one that will suit your text. Have students create an organizer as a class, in a small group, or with a partner.

Study common order—Students can also look for common orders. Types of orders can include chronological, serial, logical, functional, spatial, and hierarchical.

Standardized Tests

Standardized tests have taken a great importance in education today. As an educator, you know that standardized tests do not necessarily provide an accurate picture of a student. There are many factors that do not reflect the students' competence that sway the results of these tests.

- The diversity of our big country makes the tests difficult to norm.
- Students that are talented in areas other than math and language cannot show this talent.
- Students who do not speak and read English fluently will not do well on standardized tests.
- Students who live in poverty do not necessarily have the experiences necessary to comprehend the questions.

The list could go on, but there does have to be some sort of assessment of progress that a community can use to decide how the schools are doing. Standardized tests and their results are receiving more and more attention these days. The purpose of this series, along with creating better readers, is to help students get better results on standardized tests.

Test Success

The ability to do well when taking traditional standardized tests on comprehension requires at least three things:

- a large vocabulary of sight words
- the mastery of certain specific test-taking skills
- the ability to recognize and control stress

Vocabulary has already been discussed in detail. Test-taking skills and recognizing and controlling stress can be taught and will be discussed in this section.

Introduction *(cont.)*

Every student in your class needs good test-taking skills, and almost all of them will need to be taught these skills. Even fluent readers and extremely logical students will fair better on standardized tests if they are taught a few simple skills for taking tests.

These test-taking skills are:

- The ability to follow complicated and sometimes confusing directions. Teach students to break down the directions and translate them into easy, understandable words. Use this series to teach them the types of questions that will appear.

- The ability to scale back what they know and concentrate on just what is asked and what is contained in the text—show them how to restrict their responses. Question students on their answers when doing practice exercises and have them show where they found the answer in the text.

- The ability to rule out confusing distracters in multiple choice answers. Teach students to look for key words and match up the information from the text.

- The ability to maintain concentration during boring and tedious repetition. Use practice time to practice this and reward students for maintaining concentration. Explain to students why they are practicing and why their concentration is important for the day of the test.

There are also environmental elements that you can practice with throughout the year in order for your students to become more accustomed to them for the testing period.

If your desks are pushed together, have students move them apart so they will be accustomed to the feel on test-taking day.

- Put a "Testing—Do Not Disturb" sign on the door.

- Require "test etiquette" when practicing: no talking, attentive listening, and following directions.

- Provide a strip of construction paper for each student to use as a marker.

- Establish a routine for replacing broken pencils. Give each student two sharpened pencils and have a back-up supply ready. Tell students they will need to raise their broken pencil in their hand, and you will give them a new one. One thing students should not worry about is the teacher's reaction to a broken pencil.

- Read the instructions to the students as you would when giving a standardized test so they grow accustomed to your test-giving voice.

- As a teacher, you probably realize that what is practiced daily is what is best learned. All of these practices work well to help students improve their scores.

Introduction *(cont.)*

Reduce Stress and Build Confidence

As well as the physical and mental aspects of test-taking, there is also the psychological. It is important to reduce students' stress and increase students' confidence during the year.

- In order to reduce stress, it first needs to be recognized. Discuss feelings and apprehensions about testing. Give students some tools for handling stress.

- Begin talking about good habits at the beginning of the year. Talk about getting enough sleep, eating a good breakfast, and exercising before and after school. Consider sending home a letter encouraging parents to start these good routines with their children at home.

- Explain the power of positive thought to your students. Tell them to use their imaginations to visualize themselves doing well. Let them know that they have practiced all year and are ready for what is to come.

- Remember to let students stretch and walk around between tests. Try using "Simon Says" with younger students throughout the year to get them to breathe deeply, stretch, and relax so it won't be a novel idea during test time.

- Build confidence during the year when using the practice tests. Emphasize that these tests are for learning. If they could get all of the answers right the first time, they wouldn't need any practice. Encourage students to state at least one thing they learned from doing the practice test.

- Give credit for reasonable answers. Explain to students that the test makers write answers that seem almost true to really test the students' understanding. Encourage students to explain why they chose the answers they gave, and then reason with the whole class on how not to be duped the next time.

- Promote a relaxed, positive outlook on test-taking. Let your students know on the real day that they are fully prepared to do their best.

Introduction *(cont.)*

When practicing skills for comprehension, it is important to vocalize and discuss the process in finding an answer. After building vocabulary, tapping background knowledge, and discussing the structure that might be used in the article, have the students read the article. If they are not able to read the article independently, have them read with a partner or in a small teacher-lead group. After completing these steps, work through the comprehension questions. The following are suggestions for working through these activities.

- Have students read the text silently and answer the questions.

- Have students correct their own papers.

- Discuss each answer and how the students came to their answers.

- Refer to the exact wording in the text.

- Discuss whether students had to tap their own knowledge or not.

═════ Answer Sheet ═════

The teacher can choose to use the blank answer sheet located at the back of the book for practice filling in bubble forms for standardized tests. The rows have not been numbered so that the teacher can use the form for any test, filling in the numbers and copying for the class as necessary. The teacher can also have the students write the answers directly on the pages of the test practice sheets instead of using the bubble sheet.

═════ Summary ═════

Teachers need to find a way to blend test preparation with the process of learning and discovery. It is important for students to learn test-taking skills and strategies because they will be important throughout life. It is more important for students to build vocabulary and knowledge, to create frameworks for comprehension, and to become fluent readers.

The *Nonfiction Comprehension Test Practice* series is an outstanding program to start your students in the direction of becoming better readers and test-takers. These are skills they will need throughout life. Provide an atmosphere of the joy of learning and create a climate for curiosity within your classroom. With daily practice of comprehension skills and test-taking procedures, teaching comprehension may seem just a little bit easier.

Sentence Comprehension

Directions: Read the following sentence carefully and answer the questions below "True" (T) or "False" (F).

"I will fight with everything I have to keep the wolves in Yellowstone," says Interior Secretary Bruce Babbit, who is in charge of the national parks.

---

1. Bruce Babbit is in charge of the national parks in the United States. _____

2. Bruce Babbit's title is Defense Secretary. _____

3. Bruce Babbit wants to keep the wolves in Yellowstone National Park. _____

4. The wolves want to leave Yellowstone National Park. _____

5. Bruce Babbit is in charge of parks around the world. _____

Word Study

Directions: Make the singular words plural.

Wolf

A wolf is a powerful, meat-eating, wild dog. However, a wolf is part of a pack and, therefore, a wolf rarely travels or hunts alone. To make wolf plural, the "f" is dropped, and "ves" is added to spell "wolves." Wolf is singular, and wolves is plural.

---

1. coyote_____

2. fox _____

3. badger_____

4. eagle_____

5. bear_____

6. person_____

7. moose_____

8. rodent_____

9. mouse_____

10. puppy_____

Paragraph Comprehension

Directions: Read the paragraph below and answer the following questions.

Grizzly bears are no longer forced to strip the trees of nuts and leaves for food, because now they can eat the wolves' leftovers. There are fewer coyotes because wolves have killed some of them. That means there is more of the coyotes' favorite food—little rodents—for foxes, badgers, and eagles to eat. Even trees and plants are healthier now that bears and elk don't snack on them as much. The amazing positive changes in Yellowstone show clearly that the return of the wolves is a positive step.

---

1. Grizzly bears do not have to eat nuts and leaves because they can eat

    a. tree bark.

    b. fish and raspberries.

    c. wolves.

    d. wolves' leftovers.

2. The coyote population is

    a. increasing.

    b. dwindling.

    c. over 8,000.

    d. attacking wolves.

3. Predators of the coyotes are

    a. bears.

    b. wolves.

    c. foxes.

    d. badgers.

4. The return of the wolves to Yellowstone

    a. has positively impacted the ecosystem.

    b. has meant a significant decrease in tourism.

    c. has done nothing to reduce tree and plant damage.

    d. has made the elk migrate south.

5. The animals that have benefited from the wolves' return are

    a. foxes.

    b. eagles.

    c. badgers.

    d. all of the above

Whole Story Comprehension

Directions: Read the story below and answer the questions on the following page.

The Packs are Back

For centuries, gray wolves prowled the forests of the American West. They had few enemies until settlers arrived in the early 1800s. People feared the wild, sharp-toothed creatures. Wolves sometimes killed farmers' animals. People worried that they might attack humans, too.

Some wolves were shot. At one time, the government paid hunters a reward for each wolf they killed. By the early 1930s, no wolves were left in Yellowstone National Park. The disappearance of wolves left a big hole in Yellowstone's ecosystem. Coyotes, normally hunted by wolves, became too numerous. Foxes and badgers, which eat the same rodents that coyotes do, were going hungry. The ecosystem was badly out of balance.

To restore Yellowstone's natural balance, the U.S. Fish and Wildlife Service decided to bring back wolves. In 1995, 31 gray wolves from Canada were brought to the park. Since then, something incredible has happened: Yellowstone has come howling back to life.

Grizzly bears are no longer forced to strip the trees of nuts and leaves for food, because now they can eat the wolves' leftovers. There are fewer coyotes because wolves have killed some of them. That means there is more of the coyotes' favorite food—little rodents—for foxes, badgers, and eagles to eat. Even trees and plants are healthier now that bears and elk don't snack on them as much. The amazing positive changes in Yellowstone show clearly that the return of the wolves is a positive step.

"Ecological change seldom happens before your eyes," says John Varley, a director at Yellowstone National Park. "I never imagined we'd see it."

However, some people have ignored the improvement of the balance of nature in the park. Ranchers near the park still want to get rid of their old enemy. Since 1995, roaming wolves have killed 84 sheep and seven cattle. An environmental group has paid the ranchers to replace the animals. But, complains rancher Vern Keller, "There's the stress of not knowing if wolves are in the area or when they'll strike."

Keller and others went to court. They argued that the way in which Yellowstone's new wolves were brought into the park was illegal. In December, 1997, a judge agreed and ordered the wolves to be removed. Environmental groups are fighting the decision. "It was an order to take 10 steps backward," says Thomas France of the National Wildlife Federation.

The original 31 animals have multiplied to between 150 and 200. They cannot be shipped back to Canada, because their old territory has been taken over by other wolves. Zoos aren't likely to take them. Says Yellowstone scientist Douglas Smith: "The options could come down to one thing—killing them."

The judge's decision is still being appealed. In fact, the case may go all the way to the Supreme Court. "I will fight with everything I have to keep the wolves in Yellowstone," says Interior Secretary Bruce Babbitt, who is in charge of the national parks. The wolves are used to being the focus of a fight. It's been that way for more than 100 years. However, humans must not let the great success of the wolves be reversed.

Whole Story Comprehension (cont.)

Directions: After you have read the story on the previous page, answer the questions below.

1. Wolves cannot return to Canada because
    a. their old territory has been taken over.
    b. they have been Americanized.
    c. they would be shot.
    d. the wolves are an essential part in maintaining Yellowstone's balance.
    e. both a and d

2. Enemies of the gray wolf
    a. were the settlers of 1800.
    b. are ranchers.
    c. are the National Wildlife Federation.
    d. all of the above
    e. both a and b

3. Wolves were once shot because
    a. they attacked a group of tourists at Yellowstone.
    b. the government paid for each wolf killed.
    c. they had rabies.
    d. they disrupted Yellowstone's ecosystem.

4. Foxes and badgers suffered because
    a. ranchers and farmers installed fences around their farms.
    b. the wolves were their predator.
    c. the coyotes were eating all of their food.
    d. Yellowstone National Park did not provide adequate food for them.

5. In the sentence, "Yellowstone has come howling back to life," the word *howling*
    a. is a word often used to describe wolves' sounds.
    b. is a descriptive word.
    c. gets the readers' attention.
    d. all of the above

6. Ranchers complain about wolves
    a. because roaming wolves have killed 84 sheep and 7 cattle.
    b. they are unsure about where wolves are and when they might strike.
    c. because they feel the wolves were brought into the park illegally.
    d. all of the above

7. The author's opinion is that
    a. wolves should remain in Yellowstone.
    b. wolves should be removed from Yellowstone.
    c. wolves are destroying Yellowstone.
    d. wolves in Canada are mean.

8. The wolves' greatest ally
    a. is Vern Keller.
    b. is Thomas France.
    c. is John Varley.
    d. both b and c
    e. all of the above

Enrichment

Directions: Analyze the changes. All nouns that name specific people, places, or things must be capitalized. Capitalize all letters or words that need to be capitalized in the group of sentences below. Rewrite the paragraph with the correct capitalization.

Proper nouns are nouns that name a specific person, place, thing, or idea. Proper nouns are almost always capitalized.

A rancher is fighting the decision to allow wolves to remain in the park.

The nouns in this sentence are: *rancher, decision, wolves,* and *park.* None of these nouns name a specific person, place, or thing. Therefore, all letters are lowercase. Now consider this sentence.

Vern Keller is fighting the decision to allow wolves to remain in Yellowstone National Park.

At yellowstone national park, wolves are now endangered. The supreme court of the united states may hold the wolves' existence in their hands. A group of ranchers want the american gray wolf to return to canada, but the national wildlife federation believes the wolves maintain yellowstone's ecosystem and symbolize the american west. Should the wolves be allowed to remain? The courts will decide.

_____

_____

_____

_____

_____

_____

Graphic Development

Directions: Based on the story, "The Packs are Back," create a poster of the animals and vegetation in Yellowstone National Park that have benefited since the wolves have been reintroduced to the park.

Sentence Comprehension

Directions: Read the following sentence carefully and answer the questions below "True" (T) or "False" (F).

Millions of birds fly over the island of Sicily each spring on their migration to Northern Europe, where they lay their eggs.

---

1. The number of birds that fly over Sicily is in the millions. _____

2. In the fall, the birds migrate. _____

3. The migration route is from Sicily to Northern Europe. _____

4. The birds migrate to lay their eggs. _____

5. The eggs are hatched in Sicily each spring. _____

Word Study

Directions: Choose an adverb from the list of words below that best fits the sentence. Each adverb should be used only once.

Majestically

Majestically is an adverb that means with greatness, authority, and grandeur. A sentence about Anna-Maria Giordano and her plight may read, "Now the birds fly majestically over Messina, Italy, without fear of getting shot by poachers."

An adverb is a word that describes a verb. Many adverbs end with the suffix *-ly*. In the above sentence, the word *majestically* describes how the birds fly. How else can a bird fly? (slowly, quickly, gracefully, etc.)

---

       angrily   diligently   fortunately   illegally   happily

1. Bird hunters _____ shoot birds, and, if caught, go unpunished.

2. Poachers yelled _____ at Giordano when she tried to stop them from bird hunting.

3. After an injured bird heals at the center, it flies _____ into the sky.

4. Before Giordano _____ patrolled the woods looking for poachers, over 5,000 birds were shot each year.

5. _____, law-enforcement officers assisted Giordano after she received threats.

Paragraph Comprehension

Directions: Read the paragraph below and answer the following questions.

Today, Giordano, 32, is a trained ornithologist (bird scientist). She is trying to raise funds for an International Ornithological Center in Italy. The center would teach kids, researchers, and volunteers about bird watching, illegal hunting, and environmental protection. It would also house a bird hospital in which injured birds could be treated until their release back into the wild.

---

1. Giordano

    a. has been saving birds for 32 years.

    b. is 32 years old.

    c. volunteers in a bird hospital.

    d. all of the above

2. An ornithologist is

    a. a bird watcher.

    b. a bird scientist.

    d. a bird hunter.

    e. a bird.

3. In the sentence, "She is trying to raise funds . . .," *funds* means

    a. money.

    b. awareness.

    c. fun.

    d. all of the above

4. The International Ornithological Center

    a. teaches people about bird watching.

    b. teaches people about illegal bird hunting.

    c. is not built yet.

    d. both a and b

5. The purpose of a bird hospital is

    a. to treat injured birds until their release.

    b. to give injured birds medical advice.

    c. to have a hospital in the clouds.

    d. to provide a birdhouse that has birdseed with medicine mixed in.

Whole Story Comprehension

Directions: Read the story below and answer the questions on the following page.

She's for the Birds

When Anna-Maria Giordano was 10 years old, she fell in love with birds. She would go to the market in her hometown of Messina, Italy, to buy small, perky finches. Messina is on the island of Sicily, near the toe of boot-shaped Italy. Millions of birds fly over the island each spring on their migration route from Africa to Northern Europe, where they lay their eggs.

"I started buying singing birds like goldfinches and chaffinches," she says. Giordano always set them free.

Sadly, a bird set free in Sicily faces danger in the skies. Italians have a long tradition of shooting storks, honey buzzards, golden orioles, swallows, quail, and other birds winging their way north. Although hunting such birds is illegal, the people who shoot protected birds often go unpunished.

When Giordano was 15, she decided to help the birds. First, she tried to get forest rangers to enforce the hunting laws. That went nowhere. "They all made fun of me because I was just a girl of 15, and I was trying to tell them what to do."

So she and a friend created their own hunting patrol. They went into the woods every year during the migration period in April and May to look for illegal hunters, called poachers. Angry poachers would yell insults at her patrol.

When she was 22, someone set Giordano's car on fire—most likely the poachers. They even mailed her a dead falcon and a note that said, "Your courage will cost you dearly."

Giordano was bothered by the threats, but she wasn't about to quit. In fact, the abuse she suffered from the hunters helped get law-enforcement officers on her side. "It made the police understand that poaching wasn't just a joke and made them start helping us track down the poachers."

With the help of the police, Giordano has made a big improvement for the birds that fly over her home. Before she began her patrol, more than 5,000 protected birds were shot by Sicilian hunters each year. Now the number is closer to 200.

Says Giordano: "After years of fighting and discussing this problem and writing articles and letters to the newspapers, we have seen the numbers of hunters and slaughtered birds decline each year."

Today, Giordano, 32, is a trained ornithologist (bird scientist). She is trying to raise funds for an International Ornithological Center in Italy. The center would teach kids, researchers, and volunteers about bird watching, illegal hunting, and environmental protection. It would also house a bird hospital in which injured birds could be treated until their release back into the wild. Meanwhile, she works at the World Wildlife Fund (WWF) Center for the Rehabilitation of Injured Birds in Messina. She is director of the WWF's Natural Saltwater Reserve in Paceco, Italy, and she has won many awards for her efforts to protect her feathered friends.

Whole Story Comprehension *(cont.)*

Directions: After you have read the story on the previous page, answer the questions below.

1. The first birds Giordano saved were

    a. goldfinches.

    b. serin finches.

    c. chaffinches.

    d. both a and c

    e. none of the above

2. Anna-Maria Giordano decided to help birds

    a. when she was 15.

    b. because she saw protected birds shot illegally.

    c. because she loved birds.

    d. all of the above

3. Giordano and a friend went into the woods

    a. every year during the migration period in April and May.

    b. to look for illegal bird hunters.

    c. to protect the migrating birds.

    d. all of the above

4. "Poaching" in the story means

    a. a way to cook eggs.

    b. hunting animals illegally.

    c. obtaining a hunting license.

    d. a way to describe a bird's flight.

5. Law enforcement assisted Giordano

    a. when she was 15.

    b. when Giordano received threats from poachers.

    c. when she called "911."

    d. now that the International Ornithological Center is complete.

6. Giordano is presently

    a. working at the World Wildlife Fund Center for the Rehabilitation of Injured Birds in Messina.

    b. the director of the World Wildlife Fund's Natural Saltwater Reserve in Paceco, Italy.

    c. receiving awards for her efforts to protect birds.

    d. all of the above

7. The number of slaughtered birds has declined each year for all of the following reasons except

    a. the newspaper letters

    b. the articles educating people about birds

    c. Giordano hired several retired military personnel to help patrol the woods

    d. the police tracked down several poachers

8. In the sentence, "Sadly, a bird set free in Sicily faces danger in the skies," the word *sadly* is

    a. a noun.

    b. a verb.

    c. an adverb.

    d. an adjective.

Enrichment

When Anna-Maria Giordano wanted to learn more about the birds she wanted to protect, she probably conducted research to learn more about the birds in Messina, Italy. Where could she learn about these birds? She could look through books, encyclopedias, Web sites, and field guides. Research is a fun and challenging way to learn new things.

The birds that Anna-Maria Giordano helped rescue in Italy were storks, honey buzzards, golden orioles, swallows, quails, and falcons.

What birds are found in your backyard? Describe at least three birds, researching as needed. Describe nesting, eating, and other characteristics that distinguish them from other birds.

Bird 1: _____

Bird 2: _____

Bird 3: _____

What is your state bird? Why? _____

_____

Describe this bird. Research as needed.

_____

_____

_____

_____

_____

_____

_____

_____

Graphic Development

Directions: Use the map of Italy to clearly show the migration route as described in the story. Highlight Messina, Italy, and any other information that you feel is important to include.

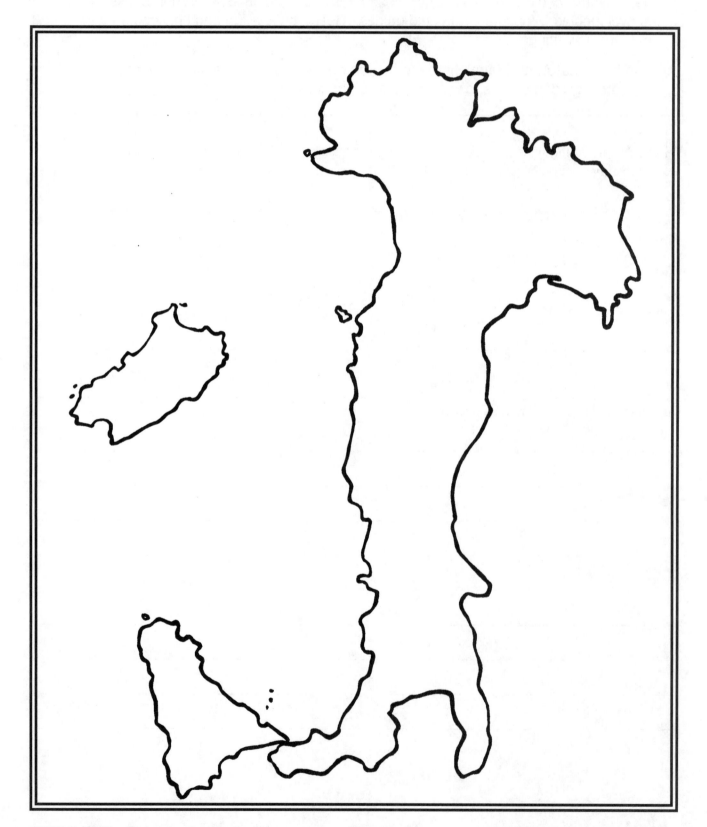

Sentence Comprehension

Directions: Read the following sentence carefully and answer the questions below "True" (T) or "False" (F).

Henry D. Flipper graduated from the U.S. Military Academy at West Point, New York, in 1877, after enduring four years of loneliness and insults because of his race.

---

1. Henry D. Flipper left West Point because he was homesick. _____

2. One U.S. Military Academy is at West Point, New York. _____

3. When Flipper graduated from West Point, he was lonely. _____

4. In 1877, Flipper was accepted at the U.S. Military Academy at West Point. _____

5. Flipper endured four years of insults because of his race. _____

Word Study

Directions: Read the sentences and write the correct definition number for each.

Race

The word "race" has many meanings. Study the following definitions:

1. Noun: A body of people united by a common history or nationality.

2. Noun: Humanity as a whole.

3. Noun: A competition.

4. Verb: A rapid onward movement.

---

1. With the depletion of the ozone layer, the entire human _____ will be affected.

2. I _____ ahead in my homework so I have time to play before bedtime.

3. The marathon runners waited for the _____ to begin.

4. The Amish are a _____ of people who have the same religious beliefs.

Paragraph Comprehension

Directions: Read the paragraph below and answer the following questions.

> After the trial, the judge said the charges were probably motivated by racism. He recommended a light punishment. But President Chester A. Arthur rejected this: Flipper was forced out of the service. After his dishonorable discharge from the Army, Flipper continued to serve his country. He worked for the Justice and Interior departments and became a respected engineer and historian. He tried, unsuccessfully, to clear his name. In 1940, Flipper died at age 84.

1. After the army, Flipper

    a. worked for the Justice and Interior departments.

    b. became an engineer and historian.

    c. served his country.

    d. all of the above

2. The judge at the trial recommended

    a. life imprisonment.

    b. twenty hours community service.

    c. a harsh punishment.

    d. a light punishment.

3. Throughout his life, Flipper tried to

    a. clear his name.

    b. find the perfect home.

    c. return to the army.

    d. become president.

4. According to the judge, the charges against Flipper were motivated by

    a. his low grades.

    b. the color of his skin.

    c. stealing.

    d. his inability to fight.

5. Flipper was named for

    a. his swimming talent.

    b. a famous dolphin.

    c. his birthplace.

    d. the paragraph does not specify

Whole Story Comprehension

Directions: Read the story below and answer the questions on the following page.

Honor at Last for Flipper

Every year, the U.S. Military Academy at West Point, New York, honors a cadet who perseveres in the face of great hardship. The award is named for Henry O. Flipper, West Point's first African-American graduate. Flipper graduated in 1877, after enduring four years of loneliness and insults because of his race. Now the worst insult has finally been wiped from his record: a charge that he was guilty of "conduct unbecoming an officer." The unfair charge led to his dismissal from the Army in 1882.

On February 19, 1999, President Bill Clinton gave Flipper a full pardon. "This good man has now completely recovered his good name," said Clinton. "Although the wheels of justice turn slowly at times, still they turn."

Flipper was born a slave in 1856, but he learned to read and write and attended college. At 17, he entered the Military Academy. During his years there, Flipper was publicly shunned by fellow cadets. Still, he stuck it out.

Flipper was assigned to frontier duty with the 10th Calvary, the famous all-black unit known as the Buffalo Soldiers. He was a good officer. Then, in 1881, his white commander at Fort Davis in Texas accused him of stealing $2,500. Flipper was court-martialed, which means he had a military trial. He was found not guilty of stealing but guilty of conduct unbecoming an officer, meaning that his behavior was not up to Army standards for an officer.

After the trial, the judge said the charges were probably motivated by racism. He recommended a light punishment. But President Chester A. Arthur rejected this: Flipper was forced out of the service. After his dishonorable discharge from the Army, Flipper continued to serve his country. He worked for the Justice and Interior departments and became a respected engineer and historian. He tried, unsuccessfully, to clear his name. In 1940, Flipper died at age 84.

Flipper's family continued his fight. In 1976, the Army gave Flipper an "honorable discharge." In 1999, seventeen relatives watched Clinton sign the pardon. "It has been a long journey," said William C. King, Flipper's great-nephew. "We learned that anger would not gain you anything; that you needed to persevere."

Whole Story Comprehension *(cont.)*

Directions: After you have read the story on the previous page, answer the questions below.

1. The Henry O. Flipper Award honors
   a. African-American cadets.
   b. physically challenged cadets.
   c. a cadet who perseveres in the face of great hardship.
   d. West Point graduates.

2. The U.S. Military Academy at West Point is in
   a. New York.
   b. New Jersey.
   c. New Mexico.
   d. North Carolina.

3. Flipper's unit, the 10th Cavalry,
   a. was all black.
   b. was filled with racists.
   c. was nicknamed the Buffalo Soldiers.
   d. both a and c

4. In 1881, Flipper's commander accused him
   a. of disobeying rules.
   b. of not wearing the correct uniform.
   c. of not saluting.
   d. of stealing money.

5. Court-martialed means
   a. setting a court date.
   b. having a military trial.
   c. attending a martial arts class.
   d. being selected as a jury member.

6. Flipper was found guilty of
   a. stealing.
   b. racism.
   c. conduct unbecoming an officer.
   d. both a and c

7. In 1976,
   a. Clinton signed Flipper's pardon.
   b. Flipper died.
   c. Flipper presented an award at West Point.
   d. the Army gave Flipper an "honorable discharge."

8. President William Clinton believes
   a. the judicial system is not working.
   b. the judicial system often moves slowly.
   c. he should present the award at West Point.
   d. the judicial system needs better court houses.

Enrichment

Directions: Revise each sentence to include a colon.

Colon

The colon (:) is a dramatic way to introduce complete sentences, lists, quotations, or dialogue. When the reader sees a colon, it means that something important follows.

Now the worst insult has finally been wiped from his record: a charge that he was guilty of "conduct unbecoming an officer."

But President Chester A. Arthur rejected this: Flipper was forced out of the service.

---

1. At West Point, Henry O. Flipper endured many hardships insults, ostracism, and loneliness.

   _____

   _____

2. Henry O. Flipper taught fellow African-Americans and cadets a great lesson. Perseverance will achieve greater results than anger.

   _____

   _____

3. President Clinton gave Flipper a full pardon. "This good man has now completely recovered his good name. Although the wheels of justice turn slowly at times, still they turn."

   _____

   _____

Graphic Development

Directions: Create a time line of Henry O. Flipper's life using the dates from the article. Write the dates that correspond to each event on the lines. Write the number that represents each event on the time line.

1. Henry O. Flipper is born _____

2. Flipper attends West Point _____

3. Flipper graduates _____

4. Flipper is accused of stealing _____

5. Flipper is dismissed from the Army _____

6. Flipper dies, age 84 _____

7. Army gives Flipper an honorable discharge _____

8. Clinton signs Flipper's pardon _____

1850   2000

Sentence Comprehension

Directions: Read the following sentence carefully and answer the questions below "True" (T) or "False" (F).

In the weekends that followed, we made rows, planted flower and vegetable seeds, fertilized, watered, and weeded.

---

1. During the week, the group worked on the garden. _____

2. The sentence is in chronological order. _____

3. On Saturday and Sunday, the group spent time on the flower and vegetable garden. _____

4. Fertilize means to add nutrients to the dirt to promote growth. _____

5. Only bean seeds were planted. _____

Word Study

Directions: Organize the five sentences below based on the transitional phrase in each sentence. First, underline the transition or transitional phrase. Then, number the sentences in the appropriate, sequential order.

Now

Now is a word that indicates time. It is often referred to as a transitional word, as well as an adverb, because it tells when. Transitional words such as now are important because they help the reader understand the sequence of events. Words such as yesterday, today, and phrases like, "When I was three. . ." and "Next year. . ." let the reader know when something happened or will happen.

_____ By lunchtime, we had filled 50 trash bags with junk.

_____ Tonight, I finally realized how beneficial the garden has been for our community.

_____ On the first morning, we cleared the garbage from the vacant lot.

_____ At the end of the first day, the lot looked better!

_____ After about two weeks, the plants began growing!

Paragraph Comprehension

Directions: Read the paragraph below and answer the following questions.

I griped and moaned the whole day. My parents were making me work on the neighborhood project, and I had better things to do. It was just the ugly, old, vacant lot across from Johnny's Shop and Go. It was full of weeds, greasy fast food wraps, old newspapers, broken glass, and every other kind of nasty trash you can think of. As I looked at it that first morning, I thought, "I bet there are snakes in there, too." I would rather have been anywhere else.

1. The narrator gripes and moans because
   - a. he is ill.
   - b. he doesn't want to work on the project.
   - c. he doesn't like his parents.
   - d. he likes the vacant lot the way it is.

2. Instead of being in the vacant lot, the narrator would rather be
   - a. in a snake pit.
   - b. eating greasy fast food.
   - c. anywhere else.
   - d. at Johnny's Shop and Go.

3. The narrator is at the vacant lot because
   - a. his parents made him go.
   - b. he wanted to volunteer.
   - c. he wants to find treasure.
   - d. all of the above

4. The author's attitude in the first paragraph is
   - a. optimistic.
   - b. proud.
   - c. negative.
   - d. eager.

5. The author's description in the paragraph
   - a. proves the lot doesn't need fixing up.
   - b. is vivid because it creates a picture of the lot and how much work is needed.
   - c. shows the beauty of nature.
   - d. is weak.

Whole Story Comprehension

Directions: Read the story below and answer the questions on the following page.

Green Thumbs

I griped and moaned the whole day. My parents were making me work on the neighborhood project, and I had better things to do. It was just the ugly, old, vacant lot across from Johnny's Shop and Go. It was full of weeds, greasy fast food wraps, old newspapers, broken glass, and every other kind of nasty trash you can imagine. As I looked at it that first morning, I thought, "I bet there are snakes in there, too." I would rather have been anywhere else.

There were twenty of us—all ages and sizes—ready to work that day. The idea that this awful mess could be cleaned, let alone made into a garden showplace, seemed unlikely. I suspect we were all wondering where to begin. Then Mr. Hernandez said, "The only way to do it is just to start." Then he divided the lot into fourths with string and assigned five people to each quadrant.

By lunchtime, I was hot, sweaty, grimy, and glad my dad had made me wear gloves. (The rusty cans and shards of glass were wicked!) We had filled fifty trash bags with junk and were ready to pull weeds. Great. Now it was time to get a nose-full of pollen and go into an allergic sneeze-fest. Did you know that weeds can make you itch?

At the end of the day, I had to admit the lot looked better. Bare, but better. My dad was starting to till the dirt. A tiller is a weird-looking machine that a person holds onto by two handles. It's kind of a personal-size tractor that you manage like a lawn mower. It has a gas motor that drives these rotating blades and pushes it along. The blades lift and turn the dirt and get it ready to plant. Watching Dad's shoulders strain and his arms jostle, I thought how he and the tiller seemed a team—like a farmer driving his mechanical, earth-eating mule.

That first day was the toughest. In the weekends that followed, we made rows, planted flower and vegetable seeds, fertilized, watered, and weeded. After about two weeks, I stopped griping. The plants had started popping up! First the lettuce, then the beans and squash. They grew so fast, I couldn't believe it! Some days, a bean plant would grow an inch. A zucchini leaf could double in size in just a few days.

Now, two months later, I like to go there every day to see what new flowers are ready to pop. The marigolds are my favorites with their fat, rich orange blooms. Lots of people in the neighborhood meet there to enjoy the sights and talk. Tonight, it suddenly hit me—what a good thing we did! I'm proud I have been a part of it. The vegetables will go to the food pantry. I'm in charge of picking bouquets for the nursing home on Fourth Avenue. But even better, an eyesore that people avoided has become a pretty patch of green—a place for everyone to enjoy.

Whole Story Comprehension (cont.)

Directions: After you have read the story on the previous page, answer the questions below.

1. The leader of the neighborhood project is
   a. the narrator's father.
   b. Mr. Hernandez.
   c. the narrator.
   d. Johnny.

2. The author includes details about how hot and unpleasant the clean-up work was
   a. to show his resentment to the project.
   b. to show how difficult the work was.
   c. because he feels a garden will never grow.
   d. all of the above

3. From watching his dad with the tiller, the author
   a. sees how important the project is to his family.
   b. sees that his dad is working, too.
   c. goes home because the job is almost done.
   d. both a and b

4. The author describes the tiller
   a. so people will buy one.
   b. so readers don't think he is lazy.
   c. so readers can understand what a tiller is.
   d. because he wants to be a farmer.

5. The author's enthusiasm toward the project shows
   a. when the tiller breaks.
   b. when he eats the vegetables.
   c. when the project ends.
   d. when plants begin to grow.

6. The purpose of describing how fast the plants grew was
   a. because the vacant garbage lot was transformed.
   b. because the author cannot believe the plants are actually growing.
   c. because it encouraged the author to continue with the project.
   d. all of the above

7. The author's attitude changed from
   a. resentment to pride.
   b. anger to enjoyment.
   c. did not alter from beginning to end.
   d. both a and b

8. The author's role at the conclusion was
   a. bouquet picker for a nursing home.
   b. vegetable picker for the food pantry.
   c. chasing rabbits and birds from the garden.
   d. planning next season's garden.

Enrichment

Directions: For the sentences below, circle the pronoun that is correct. Rewrite each sentence correctly on the lines below.

When writing a personal narrative, it is important to write using the first person, or *I* as narrator. It is also important to use pronouns such as *I, me, we,* and *us* correctly.

---

1. Mr. Hernandez will help (us/we) clear the lot.

   _____

2. Will you join (me/I) in our neighborhood project?

   _____

3. The mayor gave (us/we) certificates of appreciation for our volunteer efforts.

   _____

4. My dad will teach (me/I) how to use a tiller next year.

   _____

5. (Us/We) need to work together to make our garden a success.

   _____

6. Dad and (me/I) are bringing flowers to the nursing home today.

   _____

Graphic Development

Directions: Draw or illustrate the steps in creating a garden from beginning to end, in chronological order. Use a comic strip format.

1.	2.
3.	4.
5.	6.

Sentence Comprehension

Directions: Read the following sentence carefully and answer the questions below "True" (T) or "False" (F).

Puerto Rico was discovered in 1493 by Christopher Columbus and was ruled by Spain for 400 years.

---

1. It took Christopher Columbus 400 years to discover Puerto Rico. _____

2. Puerto Rico was ruled by Christopher Columbus for 400 years. _____

3. In 1493, Christopher Columbus discovered an island named Puerto Rico. _____

4. Christopher Columbus discovered Puerto Rico 400 years ago. _____

5. Christopher Columbus had relatives in Puerto Rico. _____

Word Study

Directions: Beside each sentence, write the letter that corresponds with the matching definition.

Star

The word *star* has several meanings.

   a. In astronomy, a star is a self-luminous, self-containing mass of gas. Stars are also referred to as the "twinkling" points of light seen from Earth at night.

   b. A star is a symbol that usually implies "excellent." (Think of all the stars on school papers.)

   c. A star is a person who plays the leading role in a movie, play, or sporting event.

---

1. When I visit Hollywood, I hope to meet at least one star! _____

2. Mrs. Williams put a star next to the sentence that she liked best in my story. _____

3. Before I go to sleep, I always wish upon a star. _____

4. Look! I just saw a shooting star zip across the sky! _____

5. Serena received the starring role in our school play. _____

6. There was a star next to each person's name who was in the band and also in the school choir. _____

Paragraph Comprehension

Directions: Read the paragraph below and answer the following questions.

The Caribbean island of Puerto Rico has a 100-year history as part of the U.S. Many Americans don't even realize that Puerto Rico's residents are U.S. citizens. They are, but it's a tricky relationship. Puerto Rico's residents do not pay federal income taxes, and they cannot vote for president or representation in Congress. Puerto Rico has a governor and a delegate to the U.S. Congress, but that person has no vote. The island is a commonwealth—a self-governing part of the U.S.—not a state. Puerto Ricans should vote to become the 51st American state.

---

1. The residents of Puerto Rico are

    a. also citizens of Spain.

    b. citizens of Florida.

    c. citizens of the United States.

    d. all of the above

2. Because Puerto Rico residents don't pay federal income taxes,

    a. they can't live in the United States.

    b. they can't vote for the president of the United States.

    c. they can only visit the United States for seven days.

    d. they have a high education tax.

3. "Commonwealth" means

    a. self-governing.

    b. dependent upon the United States.

    c. everyone has about the same amount of money.

    d. the government gives families a "common" monthly allowance.

4. Puerto Rico is

    a. an island.

    b. part of Florida.

    c. near Hawaii.

    d. the 51st state of America.

5. The Puerto Rican governor and delegate to the United States Congress

    a. can only vote on issues concerning Puerto Rico.

    b. are members of the 51st state.

    c. live in Washington, D.C.

    d. have no vote.

Whole Story Comprehension

Directions: Read the story below and answer the questions on the following page.

Another Star in Our Flag

The Caribbean island of Puerto Rico has a 100-year history as part of the U.S. Many Americans don't even realize that Puerto Rico's residents are U.S. citizens. They are, but it's a tricky relationship. Puerto Rico's residents do not pay federal income taxes, and they cannot vote for president or representation in Congress. Puerto Rico has a governor and a delegate to the U.S. Congress, but that person has no vote. The island is a commonwealth—a self-governing part of the U.S.—not a state. Puerto Ricans should vote to become the 51st American state.

The relationship between the U.S. and Puerto Rico would be easier if Puerto Rico became a state. Its governor agrees. "It is not valid to keep nearly 4 million U.S. citizens without their full citizenship rights," says Governor Pedro Rossello (Ro-say-yoh).

In December, 1998, the island's voters went to the polls for a plebiscite (pleb-uh-site)—a vote to change or maintain its political status. Voters had four choices. They could vote for statehood or to remain a commonwealth. They also voted for free association with the U.S. or for independence. In the election, 46% voted for statehood. Fifty percent of the voters voted "none of the above." Governor Rossello sees the vote as support for statehood, saying that "none of the above" was not a valid choice. However, for now, Puerto Rico will continue as a commonwealth.

Puerto Rico is 900 miles southeast of Miami. It was discovered in 1493 by Christopher Columbus and was ruled by Spain for 400 years. It became a U.S. possession at the end of the Spanish-American War in 1898. Today, Puerto Ricans are divided over the island's political relationship to the U.S.

Historically, many Puerto Ricans have favored remaining a commonwealth. "Puerto Ricans want to have ties to the U.S., but they want to protect their culture and language," says Roberto Prats, 32, a lawyer in San Juan. "The only status that guarantees this is the commonwealth." Some people fear that if the island becomes a state, it may lose its unique identity. However, these people should look to Hawaii, our 50th state. Not only has Hawaii kept its unique culture, but other Americans have enjoyed learning about it and experiencing it. Some Puerto Ricans object to statehood because they do not want to pay more taxes. But many citizens are willing to pay U.S. taxes in order to be a part of the booming U.S. economy.

Already, two million Puerto Ricans live in the U.S. They obviously like the American way of life. Governor Rossello thinks support for statehood is growing: "The younger generations are coming in. They're more supportive." If Puerto Ricans someday vote for statehood, the U.S. Congress must then approve a statehood plan. Puerto Ricans should vote in favor of their island becoming the 51st state.

Whole Story Comprehension *(cont.)*

Directions: After you have read the story on the previous page, answer the questions below.

1. The governor of Puerto Rico feels that if Puerto Rico becomes a state, the relationship between Puerto Rico and the United States would

   a. be easier for Puerto Rico.

   b. make traveling between the United States and Puerto Rico easier.

   c. increase Puerto Rican tourism.

   d. make Spanish the official language.

2. The correct pronunciation of Governor Pedro Rossello's name is

   a. Rah-say-yay.

   b. Ro-say-yoh.

   c. Ross-ell-o.

   d. Rose-yell-yoh.

3. The island's voters went to the polls for a *plebiscite*, which means

   a. a vote for a new senator.

   b. getting a vaccine for the Plebiscite virus.

   c. a vote to change or maintain political status.

   d. a place to purchase poles.

4. The correct number of Puerto Rican citizens without full citizenship rights is

   a. 4,000,000.

   b. 400,000.

   c. 40,000.

   d. 4,000.

5. Many Puerto Ricans want to remain a commonwealth because

   a. they like living on an island.

   b. they do not like the United States.

   c. they want to protect their culture and language.

   d. they have their own flag.

6. The Puerto Rican population in the United States is

   a. one million.

   b. two million.

   c. three million.

   d. four million.

7. The author feels

   a. that Puerto Rico should pay federal income tax.

   b. that Puerto Rico should have full-citizen rights.

   c. that Puerto Rico should remain a commonwealth.

   d. that Puerto Rico should become a state.

8. The author compares the island of Puerto Rico to

   a. Cuba.

   b. Hawaii.

   c. Haiti.

   d. the Dominican Republic.

Enrichment

Directions: Use the map below to respond to the following questions.

1. Puerto Rico is

    a. east of the Dominican Republic.

    b. west of the Dominican Republic.

    c. south of Florida

    d. both a and c

2. True or False. Puerto Rico is the southernmost state of the United States. _____

3. Through what bodies of water would you go if you started northwest of Florida and headed toward Puerto Rico?

_____

4. Puerto Rico is near to many non-USA governed islands. Therefore, Puerto Rico should not be a state. Do you agree or disagree? Why?

_____

_____

_____

5. Is Haiti an island? Why or why not?

_____

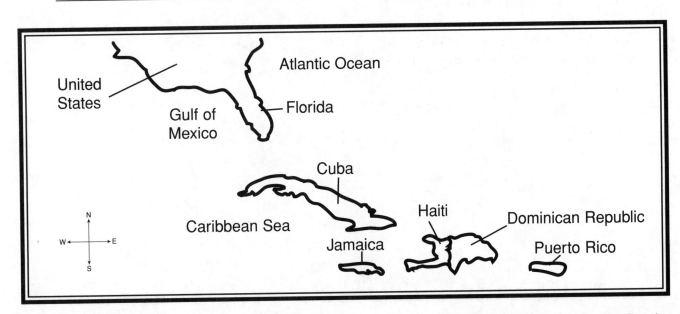

Graphic Development

Directions: Imagine that Puerto Rico is the 51st state. Design a new flag for the United States of America.

Sentence Comprehension

Directions: Read the following sentence carefully and answer the questions below "True" (T) or "False" (F).

> In my opinion, teachers perform one of the most important jobs in our community.

1. Teachers perform an important job in the community. _____

2. The author feels teachers have important jobs. _____

3. *In my opinion* means that everyone else definitely feels the same way. _____

4. Teaching is one of the most important jobs in the country. _____

5. Parents can also be considered teachers. _____

Word Study

Directions: Study the following words and their parts of speech. Then, fill in the blanks in the sentences below with the correct words.

Educate

The word *educate* means to learn or study something. Various forms of the word enable the word *educate* to become not only a verb, but also a noun, adjective, and adverb.

| educate (verb) | educator (noun) | educable (adjective) |
| education (noun) | educational (adjective) | educationally (adverb) |

1. I know it is important to get a good _____ to succeed in life.

2. For my birthday, I received an _____ game that not only teaches me geography, but also is fun.

3. Professor Bartlett received the best _____ award from his students.

4. "Even though you failed the test, I know you are _____ and will pass the retest!" the teacher encouraged the class.

5. I need to _____ myself on the Civil War for my presentation next week.

6. Our top student not only excels _____, but also athletically.

Paragraph Comprehension

Directions: Read the paragraph below and answer the following questions.

> The NEA also said that in order to keep up with the growing number of students, and to replace all the teachers who will be retiring, schools will need to hire over one million new teachers in the next ten years. Do school boards across the U.S. honestly believe they will be able to lure one million of the best minds if they are offering meager salaries that are in decline?

1. Over the next ten years, schools

    a. will need to hire one million new teachers for each school.

    b. will need to hire one new teacher for each grade level.

    c. will need to hire one million new teachers in our nation.

    d. will need to raise one million dollars to pay for teachers' salaries.

2. The NEA is concerned with

    a. the growing student population.

    b. the amount of teachers who are retiring.

    c. high teacher salaries.

    d. both a and b

    e. all of the above

3. School boards will lure teachers with

    a. high salaries.

    b. free school supplies.

    c. a lap-top computer.

    d. none of the above

4. *Best minds* refers to

    a. good teachers.

    b. brains.

    c. new text books.

    d. computer centers.

5. The salaries for teachers are

    a. rising.

    b. declining.

    c. meager.

    d. b and c

Whole Story Comprehension

Directions: Read the story below and answer the questions on the following page.

It's Time to Pay the Price

To the Editors:

I am an eighth-grade student at Fowlerville Middle School and I am upset over the way our teachers are being treated. In my opinion, teachers perform one of the most important jobs in our community. They are entrusted with educating us and preparing us for the future. The teachers I know work very hard to do that.

We don't pay teachers enough for the very important job they are doing. The average yearly salary for educators in our area is $29,000. As professionals, teachers should be paid like other professionals in our community, such as lawyers and doctors.

Of course, the question isn't, "Why would anyone want to be a teacher?" The real question is, "How could anyone afford to be a teacher—when they are paid such a salary?"

Let me tell you about my social studies teacher, Mrs. Miller. She teaches tirelessly and expertly all day. She spends her own money on certain projects for her students. She volunteers her free time on weekends to sell snacks at the football and basketball games, but she is also raising three kids. Don't you think Mrs. Miller and other teachers like her deserve to be rewarded for their commitment to students?

I checked with the National Education Association (NEA) and low salaries for educators is not a problem in just our area. It's happening all over the U.S. According to the NEA, teachers' salaries actually went down in 1998.

The NEA also said that in order to keep up with the growing number of students, and to replace all the teachers who will be retiring, schools will need to hire over one million new teachers in the next ten years. Do school boards across the U.S. honestly believe they will be able to lure one million of the best minds if they are offering meager salaries that are in decline?

What is the solution? It's simple: raise the salaries of teachers. Make the amount they earn more in line with other professionals.

Sincerely,

Bill Hunter

Fowlerville, Michigan

Whole Story Comprehension *(cont.)*

Directions: After you have read the story on the previous page, answer the questions below.

1. The author is

   a. an eighth-grade female.

   b. determined to be a teacher.

   c. concerned with teacher salaries.

   d. a student at Michigan State.

2. NEA stands for

   a. New Educators Alliance.

   b. National Educator Assistance.

   c. New Educator Assistance.

   d. National Education Association.

3. The author feels his teacher Mrs. Miller

   a. prepares him for the future.

   b. knows her subject well.

   c. is energetic.

   d. all of the above

4. Teachers should be treated like other professionals, like

   a. policemen and firemen.

   b. doctors and lawyers.

   c. actors and athletes.

   d. all of the above

5. Low salary for educators is a problem

   a. in a few places.

   b. in England.

   c. in the United States.

   d. all of the above

6. In 1998,

   a. enrollment in teacher education programs went down.

   b. teacher salaries went down.

   c. teachers went on strike.

   d. teachers formed the NEA.

7. *Meager* means all of the following except

   a. poor.

   b. puny.

   c. small.

   d. large.

8. A concern for the future of education is that

   a. individuals can not afford to be teachers.

   b. many teachers are at the retirement age.

   c. salaries are actually decreasing.

   d. all of the above

Enrichment

Directions: Write one complete paragraph about one opinion you may have about teachers. State your opinion clearly in the topic sentence. Support, prove, and defend your opinion in three to five supporting sentences and summarize your view in the concluding sentence.

A **paragraph** is a group of sentences that center or build upon one idea. The topic sentence tells what the paragraph is going to be about and the supporting sentences build upon and strengthen the topic. The last sentence in a paragraph is called the concluding sentence. This sentence sums up the paragraph. "It's Time to Pay the Price" is called an opinion piece, or editorial, because it is the opinion of one individual.

Topic Sentence

_____

_____

Supporting Sentence

_____

_____

Supporting Sentence

_____

_____

Supporting Sentence

_____

_____

Concluding Sentence

_____

_____

Graphic Development

Directions: Create a cluster based upon the word "Teacher."

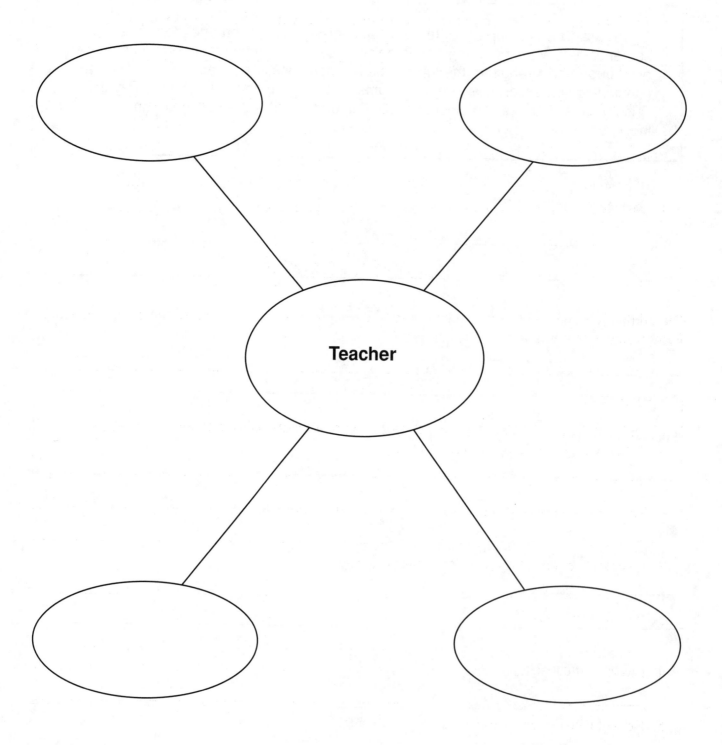

Sentence Comprehension

Directions: Read the following sentence carefully and answer the questions below "True" (T) or "False" (F).

Milo Mottola, who used to design museum exhibits, was picked in 1993 to plan a carousel for Riverbank State Park, in New York City.

---

1. Milo Mottola designed a museum exhibit for Riverbank State Park. _____
2. Milo Mottola built a carousel in 1993 for a state park. _____
3. Riverbank State Park is in New York City. _____
4. In order to design a carousel, one should first design museum exhibits. _____
5. Milo Mottola charged half a million dollars to design the carousel. _____

Word Study

Directions: For each sentence below, locate the two words that can be combined to form a contraction. Rewrite the sentence using a contraction.

He's

"He's" stands for "he is." The word *he's* is a contraction. Contractions combine two words with the help of an apostrophe.

---

1. The boys and girls could not wait for the carousel to be completed.

   _____

2. I would recommend visiting Riverbank State Park.

   _____

3. We are next to ride!

   _____

4. I wonder if they have purchased their tickets.

   _____

5. He will help design a carousel for my town next!

   _____

Paragraph Comprehension

Directions: Read the paragraph below and answer the following questions.

A carousel of fantasy animals twirls at Riverbank State Park in New York City. But it doesn't hold the usual herd of painted ponies. Instead, giant spiders pull a chariot, and a plaid zebra prances beside a two-headed octopus. These creatures were invented by kids from the Harlem neighborhood and turned into a carousel by Milo Mottola, 32.

---

1. The carousel at Riverbank State Park is unusual because

    a. the animals are not just horses.

    b. spiders pull a chariot.

    c. an adult let children assist in the planning.

    d. all of the above

2. This paragraph is an example of

    a. a narrative paragraph.

    b. a descriptive paragraph.

    c. a how-to paragraph.

    d. a chronological paragraph.

3. The words *plaid* and *two-headed* are what part of speech?

    a. noun

    b. adjective

    c. verb

    d. pronoun

4. The carousel creatures were invented by

    a. Riverbank State Park employees.

    b. kids from Harlem.

    c. Milo Mottola.

    d. New York City police officers.

5. "Painted ponies" is an example of what figure of speech?

    a. simile

    b. metaphor

    c. personification

    d. alliteration

Whole Story Comprehension

Directions: Read the story below and answer the questions on the following page.

A Carousel of Dreams

A carousel of fantasy animals twirls at Riverbank State Park in New York City. But it doesn't hold the usual herd of painted ponies. Instead, giant spiders pull a chariot, and a plaid zebra prances beside a two-headed octopus. These creatures were invented by kids from the Harlem neighborhood and turned into a carousel by Milo Mottola, 32.

Mottola, who used to design museum exhibits, was picked in 1993 to plan a carousel for the park. He decided to ask the neighborhood for creative ideas. "I knew that Harlem should be part of the job," he says.

Mottola held drawing classes in the park. Dressed as a knight in sponge rubber, he taught the kids that carousels come from medieval times. "He was very funny," says Raomei Caro, 10. Raomei's octopus was among the 32 animals and two chariots chosen for the carousel.

Mottola says it was tough to choose from the more than 1,000 drawings: "They were all my favorites!" The original drawing hangs above each animal, and the artist's signature is carved on the floor beneath.

While Mottola put the finishing touches on flamingos, kangaroos, and other creatures, the kids couldn't wait for the carousel to whirl! Says Grover Austin, 9, whose green lion joined the procession: "I'd like to ride it all summer long."

Whole Story Comprehension (cont.)

Directions: After you have read the story on the previous page, answer the questions below.

1. Carousels originated from

    a. Disneyworld.

    b. New York City.

    c. Medieval times.

    d. colonial times.

2. Why did Milo Mottola think the Harlem kids should design the animals?

    a. Kids have strong imaginations.

    b. Kids are the primary riders of merry-go-rounds.

    c. It would make them feel a part of the park.

    d. all of the above

3. In the second paragraph, the reader learns

    a. about the museum exhibits Milo Mottola designed.

    b. where Milo Mottola was born.

    c. that Milo Mottola's favorite amusement park ride is the rollercoaster.

    d. how Milo Mottola was chosen to plan the carousel and how he wanted help from kids.

4. Students like Raomei Caro thought Mottola was funny because

    a. he liked to design kids' toys.

    b. he had no adult friends.

    c. he was a stand-up comedian on weekends.

    d. he dressed as a knight in sponge rubber to teach art.

5. In the title, the word *dreams* is probably used because

    a. Milo Mottola had a dream of creating a carousel.

    b. the "dreams" of Harlem kids were analyzed by scientists.

    c. Mottola had a nightmare that the carousel would not be finished by the deadline.

    d. all of the children had to dream of a creature for the carousel.

6. The kids who designed the animals are recognized

    a. by the original drawing that hangs above each animal.

    b. by their signature carved on the floor.

    c. by being the only kids allowed to ride the carousel.

    d. both a and b

7. All in all, the final carousel consisted of

    a. 32 animals.

    b. 32 animals and two chariots.

    c. 1,000 animals.

    d. a portrait of Milo Mottola.

8. The kids whose designs were chosen for the carousel might feel

    a. proud.

    b. embarrassed.

    c. angry.

    d. jealous.

Enrichment

Directions: For each of the following animals, think of three strong action verbs that create a strong image for the reader.

What is an action verb? An action verb describes what the subject of the sentence is doing. Strong action verbs allow the reader to "see" what is happening. Strong action verbs make stories stronger.

For example, the story says, ". . . a plaid zebra prances beside a two-headed octopus." The word *prance* is a strong action verb. The author could have said "rides" or "is beside"; yet the word prance shows an image of a happy, prancing zebra.

---

1. What other action verbs could the zebra have done?

   _____ _____ _____

2. The spiders _____ _____ _____ around

   the other animals on the carousel.

3. An octopus _____ _____ _____ near

   another sea creature.

4. A flamingo _____ _____ _____ in

   circles.

5. Kangaroos _____ _____ _____ merrily.

6. A lion _____ _____ _____ across from

   a deer.

Graphic Development

Directions: The kids from Harlem designed the animals and creatures that were on the carousel. Pretend a carousel is being built in your town or city and you have been chosen to draw a creature or animal for it. Draw your original design, along with an explanation of why your design should be included.

Sentence Comprehension

Directions: Read the following sentence carefully and answer the questions below "True" (T) or "False" (F).

> Explorers also discovered something more amazing in these caves: colonies of microscopic living creatures that can survive in poisonous air and with no light.

1. Poisonous creatures live in these caves. _____

2. If something is "microscopic," it means you need a microscope to see it. _____

3. In these caves there is poisonous air and darkness. _____

4. Explorers found these colonies amazing. _____

5. All caves have poisonous air. _____

Word Study

Directions: Circle the adjectives (or descriptive words) in the sentences.

> **Large**
>
> Large is a descriptive word that means *big*. Descriptive words are called **adjectives**. Adjectives add detail and help the reader imagine and see what is happening. In the sentence, "Other days she braids her long, blond hair and puts on a helmet with a large head lamp," not only is the word *large* descriptive, but other adjectives are *long* and *blond*, which describe the woman's hair.

1. She dangles on the end of a secured rope, down the wall of a deep cave.

2. There are colorless fish that swim in the streams.

3. They discovered creatures that can survive in poisonous air.

4. They contain sulfuric acid, which can burn human skin.

5. Sparkling gypsum, calcite, and aragonite are among the minerals that shimmer in her head lamp.

Paragraph Comprehension

Directions: Read the paragraph below and answer the following questions.

"Caves are one of the last parts of the earth that aren't mapped yet," says Hose. "It's true exploring." She likes charting the unknown. "When you start "pushing" a cave—being the first one to go through—you don't know what you are going to find," she says. Sometimes she finds minerals—sparkling gypsum, calcite, and aragonite—that shimmer in her head lamp.

---

1. By using a quote in the first sentence, the author

   a. makes Hose real to the reader.

   b. can't think of anything else to write.

   c. gives valuable information about caves.

   d. both a and c

   e. all of the above

2. Hose believes "true exploring" is

   a. using a map as a guide.

   b. in your imagination.

   c. being the first person to go somewhere.

   d. going on a nature walk.

3. Caves are not mapped yet because

   a. most people are scared of caves.

   b. no one knows where caves are.

   c. nothing important can be discovered in caves.

   d. the paragraph does not have enough information.

4. Hose finds minerals in caves because

   a. she chisels the rock formations.

   b. she wants to strike gold.

   c. the minerals shine in her head lamp.

   d. all of the above

5. "Pushing" a cave means

   a. a bulldozer will knock it down.

   b. that you should not push fellow explorers.

   c. that you are the first person to enter a cave.

   d. that you will paint on the cave walls.

Whole Story Comprehension

Directions: Read the story below and answer the questions on the following page.

Into the Dark Unknown

Some days Louise Hose puts on a suit to go to work. Other days she braids her long, blond hair and puts on a helmet with a large head lamp. Sometimes she even wears a gas mask and kneepads. When she isn't dressed up to teach geology courses at Westminster College in Missouri, Hose explores and maps caves—the deeper and darker, the better.

Hose is a geologist and a speleologist, or caver. Her job is to add to our knowledge about how the earth is formed. Sometimes she crawls on her back through tight passages with rocks pressing into her body. Other times she rappels, or dangles on the end of a secured rope, down the wall of a deep cave.

For the past few years, she has gone to Tapijulapa (Tah-pee-hoo-la-pa), Mexico, during school breaks to map a cave. She and her fellow explorers found that it is full of animals that have adapted to life underground. There are vampire bats, spiders, and colorless fish and crabs that swim in the cave's streams.

They also discovered something more amazing: colonies of microscopic living creatures that can survive in poisonous air and with no light. Such creatures may give clues to what life forms are like in space. These living colonies drip down like a runny nose. They contain sulfuric acid, which can burn human skin. A photographer on the expedition named the slimy critters "snottites."

"Caves are one of the last parts of the earth that aren't mapped yet," says Hose. "It's true exploring." She likes charting the unknown. "When you start "pushing" a cave—being the first one to go through—you don't know what you are going to find," she says. Sometimes she finds minerals—sparkling gypsum, calcite, and aragonite—that shimmer in her head lamp.

When Hose was a kid in Alhambra, California, she loved to watch adventure documentaries. But the brave explorers she saw were always men. "I used to wish I was a boy, so I could be an explorer," she recalls. "Thank goodness I studied geology." Her college studies gave her confidence to discover new worlds: "Girls can and do become explorers."

Whole Story Comprehension (cont.)

Directions: After you have read the story on the previous page, answer the questions below.

1. A good description of Louise Hose's helmet is

    a. like a baseball cap

    b. similar to a bicycle helmet

    c. made of foam

    d. a hard-hat with a light on it

2. Besides exploring caves, Hose also

    a. teaches geology at Missouri State College.

    b. collects stamps.

    c. teaches geology at Westminster College.

    d. scuba dives.

3. The caves in Tapijulapa, Mexico, have shown explorers that

    a. caves are not only for bears.

    b. animals can adapt to life underground.

    c. people should live in caves.

    d. water-proof watches really are water-proof.

4. "Snottites" are

    a. dripping cave mucus.

    b. a nickname for slimy critters found in caves.

    c. what you call a sneeze in a cave because it echoes.

    d. mucus that has hardened in the shape of a nose.

5. Sulfuric acid is dangerous because

    a. it weakens cave ceilings.

    b. it causes an upset stomach.

    c. it can burn human skin.

    d. all of the above.

6. "These living colonies drip down like a runny nose" is an example of

    a. personification.

    b. metaphor.

    c. alliteration.

    d. simile.

7. The author waits until the last paragraph to tell you about Hose's childhood dream because the author feels

    a. only boys should explore caves.

    b. if you have the correct equipment, anyone can explore caves.

    c. the reader will realize dreams are attainable, whether male or female.

    d. the reader knows the explorer is a woman.

8. The author thinks exploring a cave

    a. is dangerous.

    b. is exciting.

    c. teaches others.

    d. is adventurous.

    e. all of the above

Enrichment

Directions: In the story "Into the Dark Unknown," the author defines several words or terms that may be unfamiliar to the reader. The author could have let the reader find the words in a dictionary, however, the author chose to define the terms "in context," which means the author tells what the words mean in the story. In doing so, the reader learns what the words mean and does not have to stop reading to look the words up in a dictionary.

Locate and write down three sentences in which the author defines unfamiliar words or terms.

1. _____

_____

2. _____

_____

3. _____

_____

Your turn! Choose two of the following words from the story and create a sentence for each which defines the word in context.

microscopic	adapted	geologist	geology
minerals	documentaries	charting	cave

1. _____

_____

2. _____

_____

Graphic Development

Directions: Design a cave Louise Hose might like to explore. Label minerals, animals, etc., that Louise Hose might discover.

Sentence Comprehension

Directions: Read the following sentence carefully and answer the questions below "True" (T) or "False" (F).

Pumping my legs, I pushed myself harder than I normally did at the start of a 5K race.

---

1. The sentence is about a personal experience. _____

2. 5K means the winner wins five-thousand dollars. _____

3. The race is five miles. _____

4. The type of race is unclear. _____

5. The word *normally* is an adverb. _____

Word Study

Directions: For each of the sentences, underline the present tense verb and rewrite the sentence in the past tense.

Walked

Walked is a **verb** describing how someone moves, and is in the past tense. The past tense means that something has already happened. The present tense of *walked* is *walk*.

---

1. I lead the race. _____

2. Julie has the lead. _____

3. I know how to train for a race. _____

4. I say what I feel. _____

5. I win the race! _____

Paragraph Comprehension

Directions: Read the paragraph below and answer the following questions.

We had been racing on this same course. Once the woods had hidden us from spectators, Noel had dragged his spiked shoe down the back of my right leg. The little spikes had felt like sharp fangs digging into my calf. I had tried to keep running, but it hurt too much. I had to stop while Noel zipped ahead to victory. Later, Noel insisted that the whole thing had been an accident and that he was sorry. I didn't believe any of it—accidents like that don't happen.

---

1. An example of a simile in the paragraph compares spiked shoes to
   a. sharp fangs.
   b. pointy needles.
   c. shoe spikes.
   d. porcupine quills.

2. Noel injures the narrator
   a. intentionally.
   b. accidentally.
   c. happily.
   d. depends upon the point-of-view

3. The winner of the race was
   a. the narrator.
   b. Noel.
   c. me.
   d. none of the above

4. After the narrator is injured,
   a. Noel zips to victory.
   b. he attempts to run.
   c. he stops running.
   d. all of the above

5. The contraction *didn't* means
   a. does not.
   b. do not.
   c. did not.
   d. don't.

Whole Story Comprehension

Directions: Read the story below and answer the questions on the following page.

Accident Prone

The old man walked slowly in front of us. With a smile, he raised his gun and fired. A roar exploded from the crowd of 220 as we rushed toward him. The man moved quickly, trying to get out of the way. He stumbled and just barely managed to gain safety as we raced past him. The High School Cross Country Championship had begun. Pumping my legs, I pushed myself harder than I normally did at the start of a 5K race. For a brief moment, I led the pack. Only the winding, painted path stretched before me as it snaked toward the woods. A blur of movement appeared next to me.

Without looking, I knew it was Noel Haversham. "Hey, Cliff," Noel said. "How's the leg?"

Ignore him and keep running, I told myself. But I couldn't stop the twinge of pain in my leg—a reminder of what happened two years ago . . . .

We had been racing on this same course. Once the woods had hidden us from spectators, Noel had dragged his spiked shoe down the back of my right leg. The little spikes had felt like sharp fangs digging into my calf. I had tried to keep running, but it hurt too much. I had to stop while Noel zipped ahead to victory. Later, Noel insisted that the whole thing had been an accident and that he was sorry. I didn't believe any of it—accidents like that don't happen.

Now, here we were again: the two of us in the lead, heading for the woods. Noel turned his head toward me and said, "Listen, I want to apolo—" To cut him off, I added a burst of speed to my stride, but he matched my exertion.

Then we were in the forest. Trees formed thick walls along the path. The other runners were seconds behind—it was just the two of us. He's going to do it again, I thought. He's going to use the bottom of his shoe to put himself on top!

"Keep your distance," I told him.

"Hey, you have the wrong idea about me," Noel said.

The trees crowded the path, narrowing the course. Noel swerved, closing the gap between us. I jerked to the side, trying to avoid him. Ahead, I could see the light of day. In about 100 yards, the path would take us out of the woods. Almost there, I thought.

And then I tripped. I had been so busy trying to keep track of Noel that I failed to notice an orange construction barrel used by race officials to mark the course. My foot caught the rounded edge of the barrel, and I fell, crashing to the ground.

I looked up expecting to see Noel's body getting smaller and smaller as he headed toward the finish line and the first place trophy. But instead, I saw a hand directly in front of my face. It belonged to Noel.

"Get up," he said to me, putting his hand out farther. I hesitated, and he shouted, "Hurry!"

I grabbed his hand and he helped me to my feet. "Now, let's run a real race," Noel said with a grin. With that we were off, racing toward the finish line. But not before I noticed what my collision with the barrel had caused. Scratch lines from my spiked shoes marred the barrel's orange surface.

I guess accidents do happen.

Whole Story comprehension *(cont.)*

Directions: After you have read the story on the previous page, answer the questions below.

1. The author does not tell the reader what is happening until the last sentence of the first paragraph because

    a. it makes it suspenseful.

    b. we should know it is a race.

    c. we feel the anxiety runners do.

    d. a and c

    e. all of the above

2. The twinge of pain in Cliff's leg

    a. reminds him of his injury two years ago.

    b. makes him stop the race.

    c. makes him trip Noel for revenge.

    d. forces him to hop the entire race.

3. The fourth paragraph uses a technique called

    a. foreshadowing.

    b. prediction.

    c. dialogue.

    d. flashback.

4. When Cliff says, "Keep your distance," he

    a. wants Noel to speed ahead.

    b. means he will win.

    c. is afraid.

    d. wants him to stay away.

5. Cliff falls in the present race because

    a. Noel trips him.

    b. he gets into a fight with Noel.

    c. he trips over a root.

    d. he stumbles over an orange construction barrel.

6. Noel surprises Cliff by

    a. giving him the trophy.

    b. waiting until he gets up to keep running.

    c. helping him up.

    d. moving the orange barrel.

    e. both b and c

7. What does Cliff learn during the race?

    a. There is no such thing as an accident.

    b. Accidents do happen.

    c. People are cruel.

    d. Winning is everything.

8. Who won the race is unimportant because

    a. it is what the author learned about Noel and himself that is important.

    b. neither Cliff nor Noel won.

    c. both boys were disqualified.

    d. the story would have had an unhappy ending.

Enrichment

Directions: For the sentences below, tell whether a flashback scene is necessary. Write "flashback" if a flashback is necessary, or "no flashback" if it is not important.

Flashback is a writing technique that explains why someone or something is feeling the way he or she is. It is a memory triggered by something in the present. A scene or paragraph written as a flashback provides the reader with important information necessary to understand what is happening to the character in the present.

---

1. When my mother yelled at my brother to stop, I knew just how important that word was.

   _____

2. During the soccer game, I scored a goal.

   _____

3. After I ate my fifth slice of pizza, my stomach felt like it had after Halloween.

   _____

4. The clown remembered what happened the last time he was in front of an audience, and he was determined not to let that happen again.

   _____

5. Grandad always laughs that way when he doesn't really think something is funny.

   _____

Graphic Development

Directions: Design a cross country race course that spans five miles. Use a key to note landmarks, terrain, and mileage. Draw to scale.

Key

Sentence Comprehension

Directions: Read the following sentence carefully and answer the questions below "True" (T) or "False" (F).

Mary Barley and fellow activists collected 2.5 million signatures and persuaded
Florida voters to pass a state law requiring polluters to pay most conservation costs.

---

1. Mary Barley is a conservation activist in Florida. _____

2. Florida residents experienced a tax increase due to conservation efforts. _____

3. Mary Barley passed a law requiring polluters to pick up litter along highways. _____

4. The 50 U.S. states require polluters to pay conservation costs. _____

5. Mary Barley and activists collected 2,500,000 signatures. _____

Word Study

Directions: Fill in the blank with the word that best fits each sentence.

Conservation

Conservation is a **noun** that means ensuring the long-term future availability of natural resources such as fuel, beauty, wildlife, or scenic areas.

Words that have the same root, "servation," yet mean slightly different things are:

Conserve: verb, not wasting

Preservation: noun, the saving of something in its original form

Preserve: verb, to keep from decaying

Reservation: noun, a place that is saved from being used for any other

purposes other than for what it was originally intended

Reserve: verb, to save

---

1. Please _____ three holly bushes for me.

2. In order to _____ flowers, hang them upside-down in a dry place after their first bloom.

3. Mary Barley works diligently on her Everglades _____ effort.

4. Turn off all lights when you leave to _____ electricity.

5. The _____ of the mummy allowed researchers to learn a great deal.

6. At the Native American _____ we saw authentic tribal customs.

Paragraph Comprehension

Directions: Read the paragraph below and answer the following questions.

The Everglades is about 4,000 square miles of freshwater marsh, rivers, and swamp. Most of the area is covered with sawgrass, which can grow more than six feet high and has edges as sharp as saws. The region is home to more than 850 animal species and 900 kinds of plants. Sounds like a natural paradise, right? It used to be. But after years of pollution and other abuse, the Everglades is dying.

---

1. The Everglades is 4,000 square miles of
   a. marsh.
   b. rivers.
   c. swamp.
   d. all of the above

2. The Everglades is
   a. a waterfall.
   b. a natural paradise.
   c. dying.
   d. a shopping mall.

3. Sawgrass is
   a. a plant so sharp animals are getting hurt or killed by it.
   b. a plant that dominates the Everglades.
   c. a tall plant with sharp edges.
   d. both b and c
   e. all of the above

4. The Everglades is threatened by
   a. poachers.
   b. an invasion of sawgrass.
   c. alligators.
   d. pollution.

5. The Everglades is the home of
   a. over 800 animal species.
   b. 900 plant species.
   c. 850 animal species and 900 kinds of plants.
   d. 850 people.

Whole Story Comprehension

Directions: Read the story below and answer the questions on the following page.

The Everglades Forever?

A graceful white Ibis soars through the sky. In the swamp below, lazy alligators lie still as logs. A tiny frog hops to a lily pad and lets out a big croak. It's just another day in Florida's Everglades—a unique ecosystem found only in the U.S.

The Everglades is about 4,000 square miles of freshwater marsh, rivers, and swamp. Most of the area is covered with sawgrass, which can grow more than six feet high and has edges as sharp as saws. The region is home to more than 850 animal species and 900 kinds of plants. Sounds like a natural paradise, right? It used to be. But after years of pollution and other abuse, the Everglades is dying.

Settlers of the Everglades thought the swamp was worthless. They dried out some of the marshy ground. In the 1920s, U.S. government engineers forced the Kissimmee River into a straight path and built canals and dikes to prevent flooding and to keep the water supply stable for new cities. Without its natural water supply, the Everglades began to shrink. So did its plant and animal populations. People have drained away too much water and many areas have dried out completely. Animals either leave their homes in search of water or die.

Part of the swampland where thousands of animals once thrived is packed with houses and factories. As of this year, 56 Everglades animal species are threatened or listed as endangered. Alarming numbers of wading birds, alligators, and sparrows have vanished. Can the Everglades be saved?

Many Floridians refuse to give up without a fight. They want to raise roads, creating overpasses so water can flow under traffic. They want to get rid of some canals, crack down on polluters, and help pass laws to protect the area. One of them, luckily, is Mary Barley. "The Everglades," she says, "is one of our most important natural cathedrals."

Barley is chairwoman of the Everglades Foundation. Her husband, George, a former real estate developer and fisherman, started the foundation because he worried about the Everglades' future. Since his death in a 1995 plane crash, Barley and other foundation members have fought on.

Barley has taken on the sugar cane industry. Many sugar growers use fertilizers that contain phosphorous. This chemical runs off into Everglades waters and speeds up the growth of foreign plants. These fast-growing plants use up so much water that native plants die.

Barley knows that even people who want to save the Everglades don't want to pay to correct mistakes others made. She and fellow activists collected 2.5 million signatures and persuaded Florida voters to pass a state law requiring polluters to pay most conservation costs. Thanks to her, a sugar company sold more than 50,000 acres of Everglades land back to the state to be restored. The river can run naturally again, which will help bring back native plants and animals.

Like many heroes, Barley claims she is not worthy of special recognition or rewards. She's doing what comes naturally to her. "This is how I want George to be remembered," she says, "and how I want to give back all the great things I've received in Florida."

Whole Story Comprehension (cont.)

Directions: After you have read the story on the previous page, answer the questions below.

1. The first paragraph of the story

    a. lets the reader "see" the Everglades.

    b. shows the reader the dying animals.

    c. is a map showing the location of the Everglades.

    d. asks readers to join in the fight against pollution.

2. The Everglades began shrinking because

    a. early settlers thought the swamp was worthless.

    b. an earthquake hit the area in 1920.

    c. canals and dikes were built to prevent flooding.

    d. both a and c

3. Environmentalists care about the Everglades because

    a. 850 animals are dying.

    b. 900 plants are dying.

    c. 56 Everglades animal species are threatened or endangered.

    d. both a and b

4. The animals found in the Everglades are

    a. alligators, sharks, and turtles.

    b. ibis, alligators, and frogs.

    c. turtles, lily pads, and frogs.

    d. sawgrass, alligators, and ibis.

5. Sugar-cane growers are

    a. taking Mary Barley to court.

    b. buying more land in the Everglades.

    c. using chemicals that destroy native plants.

    d. using fertilizer that encourages aggression in alligators.

6. Mary Barley can be considered

    a. a hero.

    b. an environmentalist.

    c. a polluter.

    d. a and b

    e. all of the above

7. Another title for this narrative might be

    a. "The Alligators Fight Back."

    b. "Ban Sugar, Save the Everglades."

    c. "Keep the 'Ever' in Everglades."

    d. "The Endangered Everglades."

8. The main conflict in the story is

    a. the traffic in the Everglades.

    b. George Barley's death in 1995.

    c. 2.5 million Floridians want the Everglades developed into town homes.

    d. the Florida Everglades being endangered.

Enrichment

Directions: Determine whether each sentence contains a simile or metaphor.

Similes and Metaphors

A *simile* is a comparison between unlike things using like or as.

A *metaphor* is a comparison between unlike things without using like or as.

---

1. The lazy alligators lie as still as logs. _____

2. The sawgrass is as sharp as saws. _____

3. The Everglades is one of our most important cathedrals. _____

4. An Ibis is a ballerina gliding gracefully across the blue sky. _____

Next, write one sentence with a simile and one with a metaphor using two of the words listed below:

---

frog	activists
swamp	marsh
people	highway
traffic	pollution

---

5. _____

_____

6. _____

_____

Graphic Development

Directions: Using the information in the article, draw a picture of the Everglades ecosystem. Consider what the animals depend on and how pollution is affecting the ecosystem. The picture does not need to be to scale.

Sentence Comprehension

Directions: Read the following sentence carefully and answer the questions below "True" (T) or "False" (F).

In 1996, a scientific report in *Nature* magazine explained that the lions had died from a disease found mainly in dogs, called canine distemper.

---

1. In 1996, a documentary on PBS explained the mysterious death of lions. _____

2. The lions died from attacks by dogs. _____

3. Canine distemper creates bad moods in lions. _____

4. A scientific report in *Nature* magazine explained the lions' deaths. _____

5. Canine distemper is a disease typically only found in dogs. _____

Word Study

Directions: Determine whether the word document in these sentences is a noun or a verb.

Document

The word *document* can be either a noun or a verb. The noun *document* means a piece of paper that is important in some way. The verb *document* means to make note of a particular occurrence or situation to show proof.

---

1. Hand me the document labeled "Canine Distemper in Lions." _____

2. Please sign the document near the "x." _____

3. The teacher must document the student's behavior in class. _____

4. I should document all of the headaches I have been getting. _____

Paragraph Comprehension

Directions: Read the paragraph below and answer the following questions.

Scientists studied the body tissues of sick lions and discovered the canine distemper virus. They guess that the lions caught it from hyenas, which may have picked up the germs at village dumps visited by dogs. Humans living in the area own about 30,000 dogs, and the dog population is growing rapidly.

1. Scientists found the canine distemper virus in tissues of

   a. sick lions.

   b. healthy lions.

   c. dead hyenas.

   d. dogs at the dump.

2. Scientists guess the lions contracted distemper from

   a. rats.

   b. hyenas.

   c. dogs.

   d. none of the above

3. The human population is

   a. 30,000.

   b. 40,000.

   c. dwindling because of the disease.

   d. none of the above

4. The village dumps are visited by

   a. dogs.

   b. the Board of Health.

   c. hyenas.

   d. lions.

   e. a and c

5. Because the dog population is growing rapidly,

   a. scientists know the dogs should be destroyed.

   b. scientists are concerned about the future of the lions.

   c. scientists want to close the village dumps.

   d. scientists are vaccinating people.

Whole Story Comprehension

Directions: Read the story below and answer the questions on the following page.

On the Prowl Again

On Africa's Serengeti Plain, the mighty roar of a lion is heard for miles around. Wildebeests and zebras raise their ears and run for their lives. They don't want to be a hungry lion's next meal.

But for several months, a mysterious illness silenced many of the fearsome roars. Between January and September, 1994, more than 1,000 lions died in the Serengeti, East Africa's largest wildlife park. It was what one scientist called "the most dramatic die-off of lions anyone has ever seen." No one could explain it.

A team of scientists finally solved the mystery. The lions are feeling better, too. In 1996, a scientific report in *Nature* magazine explained that the lions had died from a disease found mainly in dogs, called canine distemper.

Park rangers first noticed that the lions were behaving strangely. They were twitching madly, did not move about with their usual grace, and hid from the sun. The disease spread quickly among the lions because they constantly lick one another's faces.

"It was very sad," said Heribert Hofer, a German researcher. "You study hundreds of animals and know them as individuals. Suddenly they are dying from something you don't understand."

Scientists studied the body tissues of sick lions and discovered the canine distemper virus. They guess that the lions caught it from hyenas, which may have picked up the germs at village dumps visited by dogs. Humans living in the area own about 30,000 dogs, and the dog population is growing rapidly.

Scientists are working hard to prevent another outbreak. Giving the lions vaccination shots would be difficult, but researchers are raising money to vaccinate dogs living in the park.

Meanwhile, the lions are rebounding from the deadly virus. Two-thirds of those infected have recovered. The lionesses are eating better. Cubs are surviving longer. And once again, the king of the beasts is announcing his health with that trademark roar.

Whole Story Comprehension *(cont.)*

Directions: After you have read the story on the previous page, answer the questions below.

1. In 1994, in Serengeti, East Africa's wildlife park,

    a. a mysterious illness made lions lose their roar.

    b. a group of hyenas invaded village dumps.

    c. wild dogs roamed Africa's plains.

    d. a thousand lions were dying.

2. Canine distemper causes

    a. the inflicted to act like a dog.

    b. the infected to have really horrible moods.

    c. the sufferer to grow hair and a tail.

    d. none of the above

3. The first people to notice the lion's behavior were

    a. researchers.

    b. lionesses.

    c. park rangers.

    d. local residents.

4. In the sentence, "Scientists studied the body tissues of sick lions . . . ,"*tissue* means

    a. a thin cloth.

    b. something you use to blow your nose.

    c. cellular matter.

    d. bones and blood.

5. The lions in Serengeti died

    a. in a nine-month period.

    b. in a twelve-month period.

    c. between 1994 to 1996.

    d. between September 1994 to January 1995.

6. To prevent another distemper outbreak among lions, scientists are

    a. vaccinating dogs in the park.

    b. vaccinating hyenas in the park.

    c. vaccinating lions in the park.

    d. vaccinating all dogs in Africa.

7. Scientists know treatment is working because

    a. 2/3 of infected lions have recovered.

    b. more lions have been introduced to the park.

    c. several hyenas have escaped.

    d. cubs are surviving longer.

    e. both a and d

8. One sign of a healthy lion is

    a. a lion that sheds its mane each spring.

    b. a lion that is able to leap through a ring of fire.

    c. a lion that roars.

    d. a lion that doesn't sleep.

Enrichment

Directions: In the box below is a group of collective nouns. Match each with the correct sentence.

A **collective noun** is a noun that means a group of things.

For example, a group of lions is called a *pride*.

gaggle	pod	school
colony	swarm	bunch

---

1. On the ship's deck we observed a _____ of whales.

2. Marching like soldiers, a _____ of ants paraded into the sand hill.

3. The bear batted its paw against the _____ of bees.

4. In a bowl was a _____ of bananas.

5. When I went snorkeling, I saw a _____ of tropical fish.

6. Near the pond a _____ of geese awaited bread crumbs.

Graphic Development

Directions: Using the map of the Serengeti Plain, answer the questions below.

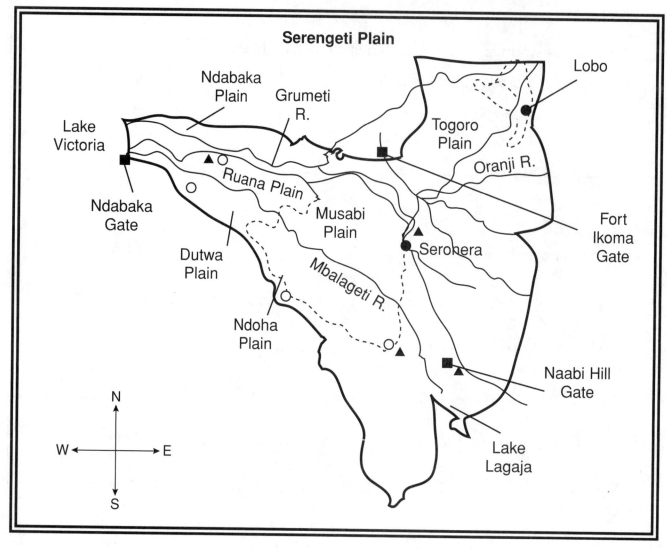

Serengeti Plain

1. What lake is located northwest of the Serengeti Plain? _____

2. The Mbalageti River deposits into what lake? _____

3. How many plains are part of the Serengeti? List them. _____

_____

_____

_____

Sentence Comprehension

Directions: Read the following sentence carefully and answer the questions below "True" (T) or "False" (F).

> Among the items stored in Ernest Shackleton's ship to Antarctica were cans of meat, a miniature pool table, a banjo, lanterns, a bicycle, and soccer balls.

1. Ernest Shackleton was headed for Antarctica. _____

2. Shackleton brought some items for recreation. _____

3. Miniature means small. _____

4. Shackleton knew the trip to Alaska would be long. _____

5. Shackleton brought his banjo because his radio was broken. _____

Word Study

Directions: Determine whether the italicized word is a noun or a verb.

> **Survive**
>
> The word *survive* means to live against challenges and hardships. The word survive is a verb. Other forms of the word are *survivor* and *survival.*

1. Ernest Shackleton is a *survivor*. _____

2. Shackleton and his crew *survived* their shipwreck. _____

3. Shackleton was concerned with the *survival* of his crew. _____

4. Would the crew left on Elephant Island *survive*? _____

5. The crew members owed their *survival* to Shackleton. _____

Paragraph Comprehension

Directions: Read the paragraph below and answer the following questions.

The sailors struggled to reach land on three lifeboats they dragged across ice and rowed through frigid waters. Eventually they reached Elephant Island, but it was deserted. So Shackleton bravely set out again with five of his strongest men. They sailed and rowed 800 miles in a tiny boat, battling high waves, winds, and severe thirst. Finally, they landed at South Georgia Island.

1. The sailors found it difficult to

    a. swim in frigid waters.

    b. entertain themselves in the cold temperatures.

    c. reach land.

    d. navigate the boat through the mountains.

2. Elephant Island

    a. greeted them with unfriendly natives.

    b. was deserted.

    c. provided them with warmer temperatures.

    d. had many elephants on it, hence the island's name.

3. That Elephant Island was deserted means

    a. the climate and terrain was like the desert.

    b. the island had no people on it.

    c. the island did not provide desserts with meals.

    d. all of the above

4. At Elephant Island, Shackleton decided to

    a. return to sea with five of his strongest men.

    b. wait there for rescue.

    c. use his cellular phone to call for help.

    d. build a fire and toast marshmallows.

5. During the 800 miles, the crew battled all of the following except

    a. severe hunger.

    b. huge waves.

    c. shark attacks.

    d. severe thirst.

Whole Story Comprehension

Directions: Read the story below and answer the questions on the following page.

Shipwrecked in Antarctica

When Ernest Shackleton packed for his trip to Antarctica in July, 1914, he seemed ready for anything. Among the items stowed in his ship were cans of meat, a miniature pool table, a banjo, lanterns, a bicycle, and soccer balls. Shackleton hoped to become the first person to travel across the frozen continent at the bottom of the world. But nothing could have prepared Shackleton or his crew for what did happen. Instead of crossing Antarctica, they made history in one of the most incredible survival stories ever.

Breathtaking photos of the doomed trip have been published for the first time in two books: for kids, Jennifer Armstrong's *Shipwreck at the Bottom of the World* (Crown); for adults, Caroline Alexander's *The Endurance* (Knopf). The pictures were taken by a photographer, Frank Hurley, who went with Shackleton on the expedition, along with 26 sailors and scientists and 69 sled dogs.

Shackleton's last stop before heading for Antarctica was a whaling station on South Georgia Island. Norwegian whalers told the crew that it was "a bad year for ice."

They were right. Upon entering the Weddell Sea, Shackleton was forced to zigzag through dangerous ice sheets, sometimes passing 400 icebergs a day! On January 18, 1915, the ice closed around the ship.

Although he was less than 100 miles from Antarctica, Shackleton soon realized he could not possibly cross the continent that winter. The crew would have to wait.

The ship was locked in ice for 10 months. By October 1915, the ice was crushing its thick wooden walls. Shackleton ordered the crew to leave. They grabbed what they could, including 150 of Hurley's precious photos.

The sailors struggled to reach land on three lifeboats they dragged across ice and rowed through frigid waters. Eventually, they reached Elephant Island, but it was deserted. So Shackleton bravely set out again with five of his strongest men. They sailed and rowed 800 miles in a tiny boat, battling high waves, winds, and severe thirst. Finally, they landed at South Georgia Island.

Four months after Shackleton sailed away, one of the men on Elephant Island spotted a ship offshore. When it came closer, the crew recognized Shackleton. They were rescued! All 28 members of the *Endurance* reached home safely. Shackleton was a true hero.

Whole Story Comprehension (cont.)

Directions: After you have read the story on the previous page, answer the questions below.

1. Ernest Shackleton's goal was

    a. to play soccer in Antarctica.

    b. to travel across Antarctica.

    c. to find gold.

    d. to take pictures of wildlife in Antarctica.

2. The photos of Shackleton's trip have been called breathtaking because

    a. they make you struggle for air.

    b. they are so worn and tattered.

    c. they inspire awe and admiration.

    d. they are three-dimensional.

3. The *Endurance* photos have been published

    a. by photographer Frank Hurley.

    b. and are on a Web site for downloading.

    c. in one book for adults, and one book for children.

    d. and reside in a museum in Antarctica.

4. One example of foreshadowing in the story is

    a. when Shackleton's banjo fell overboard.

    b. when the Norwegian whalers said the ice is bad.

    c. when the crew became ill from the meat.

    d. when the crew's letters were returned.

5. Upon entering the Weddell Sea,

    a. the *Endurance* zigzagged through dangerous sheets of ice.

    b. the *Endurance* knew the whalers' prediction was true.

    c. the *Endurance* often passed 400 icebergs daily.

    d. all of the above

6. Shackleton and his five-member crew were headed for

    a. Antarctica.

    b. Elephant Island.

    c. South Georgia Island.

    d. South America.

7. The crew remaining on Elephant Island probably

    a. felt they would never see their family again.

    b. worried that Shackleton and his crew would die.

    c. wondered if their supplies would run out.

    d. all of the above

8. Shackleton was a hero because

    a. he did not forget the commitment he made to his crew.

    b. he created a unique photo album.

    c. he saw all 28 crew members safely home.

    d. both a and c

9. When the crew left the *Endurance* in October 1915,

    a. they felt badly leaving the sled dogs.

    b. they took 150 of Hurley's photos.

    c. the ice finally melted.

    d. it ended 10 months of being stuck in ice.

    e. b and d

Enrichment

Directions: Match the words in the first column with the best match in the second column. Then, read the sentences, and find the correct compound word to complete the sentence.

A **compound word** is defined as two words that stand alone but are combined to form a new word.

Column 1	Column 2
ship	plank
life	sleds
cannon	wreck
gang	ball
off	boats
dog	shore

1. After the boat collapsed because of the ice, the sailors struggled to reach land on three

   _____.

2. Shackleton's crew was in a _____ in Antarctica.

3. Do you think the boat had a _____ for unruly crew members?

4. Shackleton had 69 dogs to pull the _____ across the ice.

5. Luckily, the crew did not have to worry about a _____ attack!

6. Four months later, the remaining crew on Elephant Island recognized

   Shackleton _____.

Graphic Development

Directions: Answer the questions based on the map.

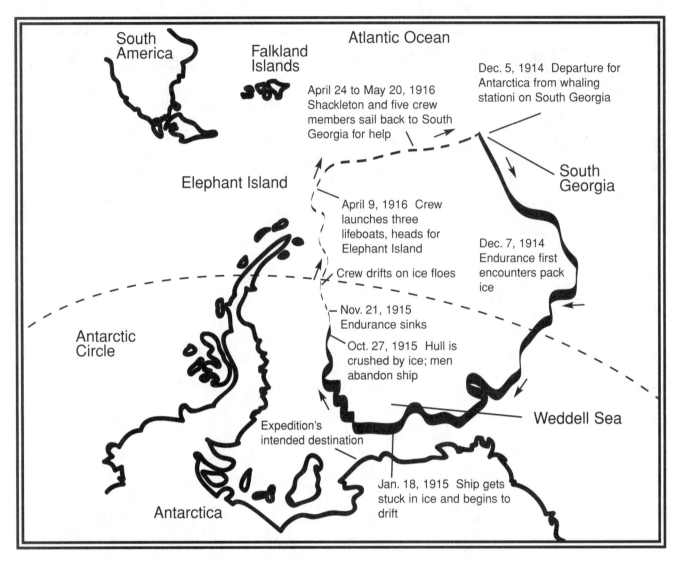

1. What bodies of water did the *Endurance* sail through? _____

2. What island was the *Endurance* departing from on December 5, 1914? _____

3. What does the "dotted line" imply? _____

4. What island did the remainder of Shackleton's crew wait on while Shackleton and five crew

   members sailed for help? _____

5. How many days was the *Endurance* forcing its way though ice? _____

Sentence Comprehension

Directions: Read the following sentence carefully and answer the questions below "True" (T) or "False" (F).

The bones a farmer found belonged to an ancient meat-eating dinosaur named Sinosauropteryx prima (Sine-o-sore-opp-ter-oiks pree-ma), which was close to the size of a large chicken and lived about 120 million years ago.

---

1. The bones found were of a vegetarian dinosaur. _____

2. All dinosaurs were enormous. _____

3. The correct pronunciation of the dinosaur is in the parentheses. _____

4. Chickens lived 120 million years ago. _____

5. The correct way of writing out 120 million is 120,000,000. _____

Word Study

Directions: Categorize the animal words below into their appropriate categories.

Carnivore

A carnivore is something that eats meat. Many people are carnivores. However, many are also herbivores, plant-eaters. Another term is insectivore, which means insect-eating.

---

tiger	alligator	frog	bat
lizard	caterpillar	koala	deer
lion	T-rex	snake	horse

carnivore	herbivore	insectivore

Paragraph Comprehension

Directions: Read the paragraph below and answer the following questions.

When and why feathers first appeared on the earth is just one puzzle scientists hope to solve by studying the area where the fossils were found. "These beds date to a time when modern mammals, flowering plants, and birds first appeared," says Alan Brush, a bird expert at the University of Connecticut. "The discovery of this site is just as important as going to Mars."

1. Scientists are learning about when feathers first appeared on Earth by

    a. completing a puzzle.

    b. studying birds.

    c. studying the area where fossils are found.

    d. studying at the University of Connecticut.

2. The area where fossils are found is also called

    a. a "Fossil Zone."

    b. a bed.

    c. a museum.

    d. "Prehistoric Place."

3. Scientists are interested in the particular fossil bed because

    a. chickens first hatched eggs there.

    b. it dates to when mammals, flowering plants, and birds first appeared.

    c. they found old feathers there.

    d. dinosaurs used it as a resting spot.

4. An expert is someone who

    a. shows off to get attention.

    b. is a beginner new to a specific field.

    c. has great knowledge or skill in a specific subject.

    d. is training to become the best.

5. Alan Brush, from the University of Connecticut,

    a. is going on the first trip to Mars.

    b. has traveled to and from Mars.

    c. parallels the discovery to going to Mars.

    d. is a dinosaur professor.

Whole Story Comprehension

Directions: Read the story below and answer the questions on the following page.

Dinosaurs with Feathers

In the summer of 1996, a farmer in northeast China was digging in a dried-up lake. He dug up some strange-looking fossilized bones. He wondered: Could these be the remains of an ancient dragon?

Not quite. The bones actually belonged to an ancient meat-eating dinosaur named Sinosauropteryx prima (Sine-o-sore-opp-terr-oiks pree-ma). The creature, which was close to the size of a large chicken, lived about 120 million years ago.

Size may not have been the only thing this dinosaur had in common with the chicken. Scientists made a surprising announcement: Sinosauropteryx might have had tiny feathers!

That's not as crazy as it may sound. Most experts think today's pigeons and parrots are related to dinosaurs. Some even argue that birds are dinosaurs, the one branch of the dinosaur family tree that has survived.

Many scientists had wondered whether some dinosaurs had feathers. But feathers are so fragile that they usually rot away without a trace. Luckily, the Sinosauropteryx fossils showed a lot of detail. "I had been skeptical of the claim that the dinosaur had feathers," says Canadian scientist Phil Currie. "Boy, was I impressed!"

Not everyone is convinced. Some bird experts suggest that the feather-like structures may be bits and pieces of scales. Whatever they are, they are not the right size and shape for flying. They may have been used to keep the dinosaur warm or help it attract a mate.

When and why feathers first appeared on the earth is just one puzzle scientists hope to solve by studying the area where the fossils were found. "These beds date to a time when modern mammals, flowering plants, and birds first appeared," says Alan Brush, a bird expert at the University of Connecticut. "The discovery of this site is just as important as going to Mars."

Whole Story Comprehension (cont.)

Directions: After you have read the story on the previous page, answer the questions below.

1. The Chinese farmer wondered if he had dug up the bones of

    a. a dragon.

    b. a chicken.

    c. a dinosaur.

    d. a bird.

2. The surprising announcement scientists made was

    a. Sinosauropteryx was a chicken.

    b. Sinosauropteryx lived about 120 million years ago.

    c. Sinosauropteryx may have had small feathers.

    d. both b and c

3. Dinosaurs may be related to

    a. birds.

    b. pigeons.

    c. parrots.

    d. all of the above

4. Many scientists have wondered if dinosaurs

    a. had feathers.

    b. live on Mars.

    c. are still alive.

    d. ever existed.

5. Scientist Phil Currie is from

    a. Connecticut.

    b. Canada.

    c. Colorado.

    d. China.

6. The Sinosauropteryx prima's feathers may have been

    a. used for flying.

    b. used for swimming.

    c. yellow and orange.

    d. for warmth.

7. The author's purpose in the story is to

    a. explain how fossils are found.

    b. relate a new dinosaur discovery.

    c. show how dinosaurs evolved.

    d. describe life in prehistoric times.

8. Scientists' reaction to the discovery of the Sinosauropteryx prima is

    a. disbelief.

    b. horror.

    c. sadness.

    d. excitement.

Enrichment

Directions: For the sentences below, place a hyphen between the "confusing" adjectives to form one word. Rewrite each sentence.

Hyphens between adjectives end a guessing game for the reader. Hyphens join adjectives to form a one-word description. Hyphens between adjectives often help the reader. For example, analyze the sentences below.

The hot air balloons drifted into the clouds.

What exactly is hot? The air or the balloons?

The hot-air balloons drifted into the clouds.

Now, there is no question. The balloon is a hot-air balloon!

1. The creatures on the space movie were strange looking.

   _____

2. My father is a full time member of the faculty at the middle school.

   _____

3. My teacher is well educated and is now going to school to get her doctorate!

   _____

4. The puppy was bright eyed when I took it from its cage.

   _____

5. A T-rex was a meat eating dinosaur.

   _____

Graphic Development

Directions: Using a Venn diagram, compare the similarities and differences between a present-day chicken and the Sinosauropteryx prima.

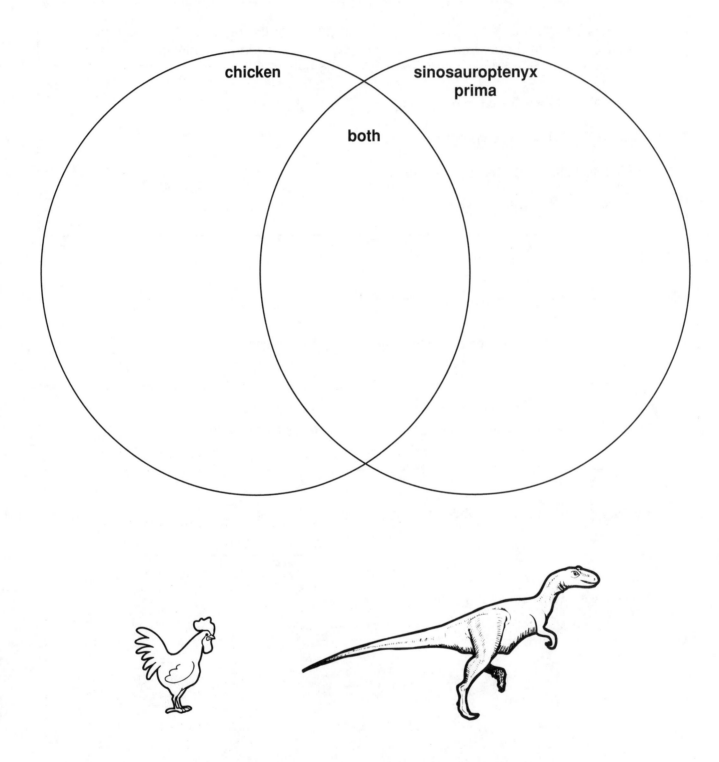

Sentence Comprehension

Directions: Read the following sentence carefully and answer the questions below "True" (T) or "False" (F).

Just one week after the NBA lockout was settled in 1999, hoops fans were saddened by the news that the game's greatest and most popular player, Michael Jordan, 35, was retiring from professional basketball.

---

1. Michael Jordan retired from basketball because of the lockout. _____

2. The NBA stands for "National Basketball Association." _____

3. Michael Jordan wore number 35. _____

4. Michael Jordan is considered the most popular and best basketball player. _____

5. After 35 years of NBA basketball, Michael Jordan retired. _____

Word Study

Directions: Write the letter of the appropriate definition for each sentence below.

Retire

Retire is a verb that has multiple meanings.

   a.   to withdraw, as for rest or seclusion
   b.   to go to bed
   c.   to give up working because of advancing age
   d.   to remove from active military service
   e.   (in baseball) to put out
   f.   (for a publication) to remove from circulation

---

1. Because only four people subscribed to the magazine, the editors decided to retire *Funny Faces* the following year. _____

2. When my uncle was 65 years old, he retired and moved to Florida. _____

3. When my mom retired from the army, she became a volunteer firefighter. _____

4. The pitcher retired the opposing team by striking out all three batters! _____

5. I retired to bed after a tiring, yet fun, day sledding. _____

6. Grandpa retired to his hammock to read before dinner. _____

Paragraph Comprehension

Directions: Read the paragraph below and answer the following questions.

Jordan played 13 seasons in the NBA, all with the Chicago Bulls. He led them to six world championships. After being named Rookie of the Year in 1984, he led the league in scoring 10 times. He was voted Most Valuable Player in the finals six times and in the regular season five times.

1. After being Rookie of the Year in 1984, Michael Jordan

 a. was the most valuable player.

 b. led his team to a world championship.

 c. began his NBA career.

 d. both a and b

2. Michael Jordan was Rookie of the Year. *Rookie* means

 a. a Star Wars character.

 b. a red cookie.

 c. a first-season team member.

 d. a basketball player.

3. Jordan played 13 seasons with

 a. the Chicago Bulls.

 b. the LA Lakers.

 c. the Chicago Cubs.

 d. the Chicago Bears.

4. *Led the league in scoring* means

 a. taking the most shots.

 b. getting the most 3-point shots.

 c. showing the team how to shoot correctly.

 d. scoring the most points.

5. Jordan played basketball for

 a. 13 seasons.

 b. 10 seasons.

 c. five seasons.

 d. six seasons.

Whole Story Comprehension

Directions: Read the story below and answer the questions on the following page.

Game Over!

It was the end of the era of air. Just one week after the NBA lockout was settled in 1999, hoops fans were saddened by the news that the game's greatest and most popular player, Michael Jordan, 35, was retiring from professional basketball.

"Mentally, I'm exhausted," Jordan explained at a news conference in Chicago. "I've accomplished everything I could as an individual."

Asked if he had lost his desire to play, Jordan said that while "the desire is always going to be there . . . this is the perfect time for me to walk away from the game. I'm at peace with that."

Anyone who has ever seen Jordan play knows how he got his nickname, Air Jordan. Without wings and without wires, he seemed to fly toward the basket. Gravity? What's gravity?

Fans around the world were moved by his announcement. A newspaper headline in Beijing, China, said, "FLYING MAN JORDAN IS COMING BACK TO EARTH." In China, the Bulls are known, and greatly loved, as "the Oxen."

Jordan played 13 seasons in the NBA, all with the Chicago Bulls. He led them to six world championships. After being named Rookie of the Year in 1984, he led the league in scoring 10 times. He was voted Most Valuable Player in the finals six times and in the regular season five times.

Jordan hangs up his sneakers with the highest scoring average in NBA history. He is third on the all-time scoring list, after Kareem Abdul-Jabbar and Wilt Chamberlain, who had longer careers.

Of course, Jordan retired from the NBA once before, in 1993. Eighteen months later, after attempting to play minor league baseball, Jordan was back on the court with the Bulls.

Asked if he might return again, Jordan answered that while he was 99.9% certain that he wouldn't, he would "never say never." But this time, Jordan seems intent on staying retired. He can't wait to pick up his kids from school and "watch them play one-on-one." Said His Airness: "I'm just going to enjoy life and do some of the things I've never done before." If anyone has earned that right, it's Michael Jordan. We'll miss him.

Whole Story Comprehension *(cont.)*

Directions: After you have read the story on the previous page, answer the questions below.

1. When Michael Jordan states, "Mentally, I'm exhausted," *mentally* means

    a. his muscles.

    b. his mind.

    c. his feet.

    d. his heart.

2. Michael Jordan's nickname is "Air Jordan" because

    a. he jumps in the air after he scores a basket.

    b. he takes deep breaths of air before shooting.

    c. he seems to fly toward the basket.

    d. all of the above

3. The author's attitude toward Michael Jordan is

    a. jealousy.

    b. hostility.

    c. respect.

    d. sadness.

4. Jordan retired from the Bulls in

    a. 1993.

    b. 1999.

    c. 1984.

    d. both a and b

5. Michael Jordan has also

    a. played major league baseball.

    b. played minor league baseball.

    c. coached professional basketball.

    d. run the Boston marathon.

6. Jordan is looking forward to retirement because

    a. life as a professional basketball player is demanding.

    b. he wants to be with his children.

    c. he wants to do new things.

    d. all of the above

7. If Jordan continued playing basketball, the author feels Jordan would have been

    a. injured.

    b. traded to another team.

    c. elected president.

    d. number one on the all-time scoring list.

8. Number One on the all-time scoring list is

    a. Michael Jordan.

    b. Kareem Abdul-Jabbar.

    c. Wilt Chamberlain.

    d. Magic Johnson.

Enrichment

Directions: Each sentence below contains a word or series of words that can be shortened with an acronym. Locate these words and rewrite these sentences with the correct acronym.

An **acronym** is a word formed from the initial letters or parts of a series of words, as in NBA, which stands for National Basketball Association. Michael Jordan also won an MVP award, or Most Valuable Player. An acronym is an abbreviated term.

For example, many of us say "DJ" as opposed to "disc jockey." The acronym means the same thing as the elongated definition. Acronyms are accepted as correct and proper terms. Most people know the luxury car as "BMW," and not "Bavarian Motor Works."

---

1. Please let me know if you are attending the holiday party as soon as possible.

   _____

2. The group of students against drunk driving is holding its first meeting in room 214 at 3 o'clock.

   _____

3. Because we had a sports utility vehicle, we were able to drive over the rocky terrain.

   _____

4. I was voted most valuable player for the soccer season!

   _____

5. The package was delivered by the United Parcel Service.

   _____

Graphic Development

Directions: Create your own acronym using your first name for the letters. Draw this acronym vertically with illustrations. Remember, your acronym must be a phrase and not simply words!

Think of acronyms for the following:

Your Name: _____

a group against those who litter

a vehicle that can travel on land, water, and air

Sentence Comprehension

Directions: Read the following sentence carefully and answer the questions below "True" (T) or "False" (F).

More than a thousand years ago, Erik the Red, a Viking Explorer, left his home in Iceland and discovered a rich supply of fish, whale, walrus, and seal in uninhabited Greenland's waters.

---

1. Erik the Red was a Viking explorer from Iceland. _____
2. Erik the Red caught more than 1,000 fish on his expedition. _____
3. "Uninhabited" means neither animal nor person are able to live in a particular place. _____
4. Erik the Red shared his voyage on a talk-show. _____
5. Animals found in Greenland's waters were fish, seal, walrus, and whale. _____

Word Study

Directions: Combine each group of sentences below to form one sentence.

Greenland

Greenland is the world's largest island, and because four-fifths of the island is covered in ice, the only habitable areas are two small coastal strips. The word *Greenland* is also a compound word, or two separate words formed to be *one—* *green* and *land*. Not only can words be combined, but sentences can also be combined to form longer, more detailed, and less choppy sentences.

---

1. Greenland is an island.
   Greenland is the largest island in the world.

   _____

2. Warriors explored Greenland.
   Tradesmen explored Greenland.

   _____

3. Viking families lived in homes along narrow inlets.
   The narrow inlets were called fjords.

   _____

Paragraph Comprehension

Directions: Read the paragraph below and answer the following questions.

Like a freezer, Greenland's cold climate has preserved traces of these ancient settlements. Scientists thought they had found them all until 1992, when Inuit (In-oo-it) hunters stumbled across some unusual pieces of wood floating into a fjord near the capital city of Nuuk. They had found a lost Viking settlement.

1. Greenland preserved traces of ancient settlements because

    a. the people who once lived there buried "time capsules."

    b. Erik the Red left a diary.

    c. its climate is like a freezer.

    d. none of the above

2. In 1992,

    a. a lost Viking settlement was found.

    b. Inuit hunters floated by on a piece of wood.

    c. Vikings finally told their story.

    d. both a and c

3. Nuuk is

    a. a type of sandal with multiple leather straps.

    b. an animal in Greenland.

    c. a capital city.

    d. an island.

4. *Preserved* means

    a. to serve on a jury.

    b. a jelly or jam.

    c. to protect from decay or change.

    d. setting the table.

5. Scientists believed

    a. all Viking settlements had been found.

    b. Erik the Red was an imaginary character.

    c. the unusual pieces of wood were a hoax.

    d. Vikings were fictitious until the settlement near Nuuk was found.

Whole Story Comprehension

Directions: Read the story below and answer the questions on the following page.

How Vikings Lived

Greenland is not very green at all. Most of the world's largest island is frozen, buried beneath endless fields of snow.

More than a thousand years ago, Erik the Red, a Viking explorer, left his home in Iceland and discovered a rich supply of fish, whale, walrus, and seal in uninhabited Greenland's waters. But he needed help to harvest the riches. He guessed that an attractive name might lure fellow Vikings from their cold homeland to an even colder place. So he called the new land Greenland.

Some Vikings must have been tricked by the name. About 5,000 of them packed up longships and made the dangerous crossing. Warriors and tradesmen began exploring. Families set up homes along the narrow inlets, called *fjords* (fee-yords).

Like a freezer, Greenland's cold climate has preserved traces of these ancient settlements. Scientists thought they had found them all until 1992, when Inuit (In-oo-it) hunters stumbled across some unusual pieces of wood floating into a fjord near the capital city of Nuuk. They had found a lost Viking settlement.

Now a team of archaeologists from around the world has finished the painstaking job of exploring it. Known as the "village beneath the sand," the settlement was actually a large farm where Vikings lived for more than 300 years. Six buildings of stone and peat (rotted moss and other plants) had up to 30 rooms each.

Digging through ancient storerooms and kitchens, the scientists found a treasure chest of Viking daily life: kitchen utensils, walrus-tooth dice, and reindeer-bone necklaces. Miniature boats and wooden boxes may have been children's toys. "It was a hard life," says Danish archaeologist Jette Arneborg, "but not without its comforts."

Why was the farm abandoned? Viking colonies began disappearing from Greenland in the 1300s. Arneborg suggests that "the weather got worse and trade dried up. Europe was no longer interested in the materials that Greenland could provide."

Whole Story Comprehension *(cont.)*

Directions: After you have read the story on the previous page, answer the questions below.

1. Greenland was named

    a. for its lush green landscape.

    b. for its tropical climate.

    c. to lure fellow Vikings there.

    d. for Erik the Green.

2. How many Vikings joined Erik the Red in journeying to Greenland?

    a. about 5,000

    b. about 500

    c. about 300

    d. the entire Viking population

3. *Peat* is

    a. the name of Erik the Red's father, Peat the Red.

    b. rotted moss and other plants.

    c. how the Vikings pronounced the English word for "feet."

    d. a Danish archaeologist.

4. Scientists estimate Vikings lived in the village

    a. for 3,000 years.

    b. more than 300 years.

    c. since 1992.

    d. since 1300.

5. The Viking farm was abandoned because

    a. the ice and snow melted.

    b. Vikings heard about the United States.

    c. the weather worsened and trade stopped.

    d. animals, like fish and whales, became extinct.

6. Jewelry may have been made from reindeer bone and walrus teeth because

    a. thieves would not want to steal it.

    b. those were the materials available.

    c. the Vikings considered them valuable.

    d. both b and c

    e. all of the above

7. The "village" consisted of

    a. 30 buildings, each with up to six rooms.

    b. a six-story building, with 30 rooms on each floor.

    c. 300 buildings.

    d. six buildings with up to 30 rooms each.

8. Viking colonies began disappearing for all of these reasons except

    a. the weather became increasingly colder.

    b. trade was ending.

    c. all of the whales, walrus, fish, and seal had been killed.

    d. Europe was not interested in trading.

Enrichment

Directions: Read "Viking Vitals" and answer the "True" (T) or "False" (F) questions that follow.

Viking Vitals

- Vikings probably got their name from the Old Norse verb *vika*, which means "to go off." They left their homes in Scandinavia to trade—and raid—in Europe from about 800 to 1100.

- Vikings treasured their fierce weapons. They gave the heavy swords, spearheads, and battle-axes nicknames like "Leg Biter" and "Long and Sharp."

- Vikings wore helmets with horns, not during battle, but during prayer to gods like Throe, the god of thunder. They wore thin leather caps for war.

- Vikings wrote by inscribing words on stone, using an ancient and mysterious system of letters and symbols called *runes*.

- Viking ships had a high prow (front) and high stern (back) for smoother rides in rough seas. Heroes were buried in huge graves with their ships; it was believed that they would sail on in the afterworld.

---

1. Vikings left Scandinavia to trade and raid in Europe. _____

2. Vikings gave their weapons nicknames. _____

3. Vikings wore helmets with horns during battle. _____

4. Vikings wrote in a mysterious systems of letters called runes. _____

5. Deceased Viking heroes were put on their ship and let adrift at sea to their afterlife. _____

Graphic Development

Directions: Imagine you are a travel agent from "Erik the Red's Travel Headquarters." You are planning a tour for fifth-graders to Greenland to explore a Viking settlement. To encourage participation, use the map of Greenland below to highlight all of the activities to do when visiting the frozen continent. Use the story for details.

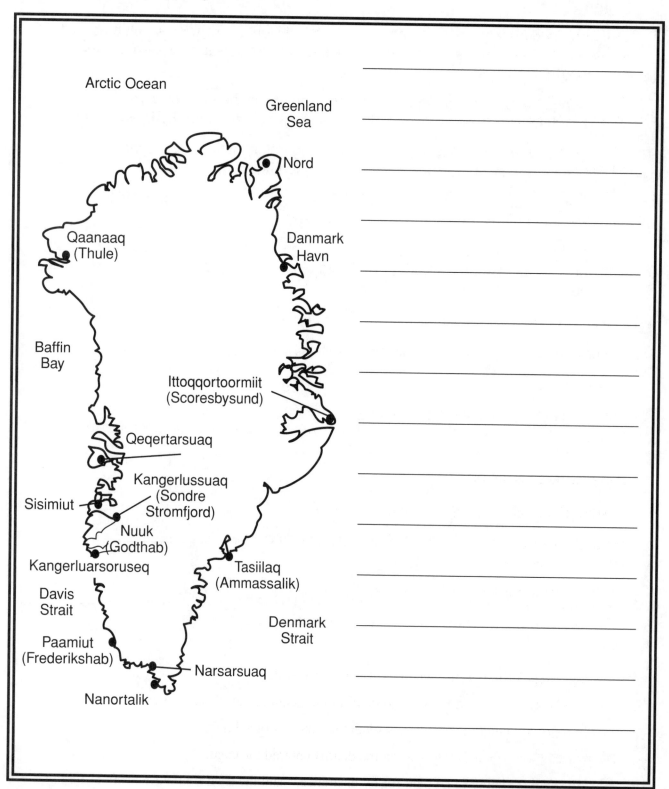

Sentence Comprehension

Directions: Read the following sentence carefully and answer the questions below "True" (T) or "False" (F).

> Recently Peter Kertesz removed an infected tusk from a five-ton zoo elephant in Germany, using a four-inch drill bit powered by a 60-pound motor.

1. The elephant's tusk weighed five tons. _____

2. Kertesz used a German tool to take out the elephant's tusk. _____

3. The size and weight of the drill gives an idea how big the job was and emphasizes the size of the patient's tusk. _____

4. Elephants' tusks, like a person's teeth, can become infected. _____

5. The elephant's tusk became infected during his stay at the zoo. _____

Word Study

Directions: For the sentences below, circle the correct form of *its*.

> **It's and Its**
>
> The words *it's* and *its* are often confused. The word *it's* is a contraction that means *it is*. If you can replace the "it's" in a sentence with *it is*, then the appropriate spelling is *it's*. However, *its* means possession or ownership of something.
>
> Consider the following examples:
>
> *The elephant had its teeth brushed.*
>
> Here, the word *its* refers to the elephant's teeth. Therefore, it is ownership, and no apostrophe is needed.
>
> *"It's time for a dental checkup!" called the dentist.*
>
> *It is* time for a dental checkup. This time an apostrophe is needed.

1. The dog wagged (its/it's) tail when the veterinarian exited the room.

2. The vet whispered, "(Its/It's) going to be difficult cleaning the snake's fangs."

3. "(Its/It's) not too late to get braces," thought the buck-toothed llama.

4. The tiger showed (its/it's) fangs when the dentist entered the cage.

5. "Luckily (its/it's) going to be paid for by insurance," said the shark before his annual cleaning.

Paragraph Comprehension

Directions: Read the paragraph below and answer the following questions.

Kertesz, 52, belongs to a rare breed of dentists who treat animals, from aardvarks to zebras. It all started when a veterinarian asked the dentist to pull teeth from a domestic cat. "Never again," he thought. But soon he was taking on bigger cats—lions, tigers, and jaguars—and then elephants (which have molars the size of bricks), camels, bears, monkeys, wolves, and even whales. He has treated about 50 species in all.

---

1. Kertesz is a dentist who

    a. has treated 52 animals.

    b. said "never again" to working with animals, and meant it.

    c. treats all types of animals.

    d. has large molars.

2. The author uses the phrase "aardvarks to zebras"

    a. to show the dentist treats animals from "A" to "Z."

    b. to be funny.

    c. to prove he knows the alphabet.

    d. because both are vegetarians.

3. Kertesz's work with animals began

    a. when a veterinarian asked him for help with an animal.

    b. after he completed veterinary school.

    c. after noticing plaque on the animals' teeth at the local zoo.

    d. none of the above

4. The size of an elephant's molars are compared to

    a. cement blocks.

    b. the shape of a peanut.

    c. Elephants do not have molars.

    d. bricks.

5. "Cats" include

    a. house cats.

    b. lions.

    c. tigers.

    d. jaguars.

    e. all of the above

Whole Story Comprehension

Directions: Read the story below and answer the questions on the following page.

Open Wide, Don't Bite

Dentist Peter Kertesz of London, England, has the wildest patients in the world. On Fridays, after a week of treating humans, Kertesz sees four-legged patients with very large teeth.

Kertesz, 52, belongs to a rare breed of dentists who treat animals, from aardvarks to zebras. It all started when a veterinarian asked the dentist to pull teeth from a domestic cat. "Never again," he thought. But soon he was taking on bigger cats—lions, tigers, and jaguars—and then elephants (which have molars the size of bricks), camels, bears, monkeys, wolves, and even whales. He has treated about 50 species in all.

Recently he removed an infected tusk from a five-ton zoo elephant in Germany. He used a four-inch drill bit powered by a 60-pound motor. Drugs keep the animals quiet and pain-free while Kertesz works, along with a team of vets and assistants.

Large animals, such as lions, are easiest to work with, he says, because there is so much room in their mouths. The toughest patients: insect-eating aardvarks, whose mouths, while long, open only about an inch.

Kertesz has taken his dental skills to eight countries. Most of his work is for zoos, but circuses and veterinary hospitals call him, too. Kertesz has worked on Siberian tigers in Russia, an elephant in Spain, and a gorilla, a jaguar, badgers, deer, and foxes in England.

One bad tooth can keep a beast from hunting, eating, and even mating. Kertesz's dental work helps animals live longer and healthier lives. "The mouth is the gateway to the existence of all animals," he says.

Whole Story Comprehension (cont.)

Directions: After you have read the story on the previous page, answer the questions below.

1. Dentist Peter Kertesz treats animals
   a. only on Fridays.
   b. Monday through Friday.
   c. in the summer.
   d. while visiting zoos.

2. The animals let Kertesz work on their teeth because
   a. the animals know how painful tooth decay is.
   b. of the cotton candy and other "junk" food people feed them.
   c. of the drugs that keep them still and free from pain.
   d. they want to have white teeth.

3. The easiest animals to work on are
   a. those with small mouths.
   b. those with large, roomy mouths.
   c. those with false teeth.
   d. those who brush regularly.

4. Most of Kertesz's animal work is done for
   a. zoos.
   b. circuses.
   c. veterinary hospitals.
   d. a and b
   e. all of the above

5. Aardvarks are tough patients because
   a. their mouths open only one inch.
   b. they cannot floss insects out of their teeth.
   c. they are insect-eating.
   d. insects cause tooth decay.

6. Good dental health is important in animals because
   a. one bad tooth can prevent mating.
   b. a painful mouth can prevent an animal from eating.
   c. animals can smile, too.
   d. a and b

7. The title "Open Wide, Don't Bite"
   a. shows the potential danger in working on an animal's mouth.
   b. is what Dr. Kertesz tells his patients before beginning treatment.
   c. foreshadows an animal's attack on Dr. Kertesz.
   d. indicates how large an animal's mouth is.

8. Kertesz's favorite animal to work on is
   a. the Siberian tiger.
   b. Mitsos, a former dancing bear.
   c. humans.
   d. not specified in the article.

Enrichment

Directions: Read the sentences in the box below and put them in chronological order.

When writing a how-to paragraph, it is important to write in chronological order so the reader is clear on the proper steps and the order of steps.

How to Brush Your Teeth

Brush up and down, side to side, scrubbing and polishing each tooth for at least one minute.

Squeeze a pea-sized amount of toothpaste onto the brush.

Rinse your mouth with clean water, swirl around mouth, and spit into sink.

Moisten the toothbrush slightly.

Rinse toothbrush and allow to air dry.

Get your toothbrush.

---

1. _____

2. _____

3. _____

4. _____

5. _____

6. _____

Graphic Development

Directions: Read the following information about teeth. Based upon the information provided, use the picture of the mouth to label the different types of teeth.

Teeth are for breaking food into soft, small pieces for swallowing. Incisors are the teeth at the front of the mouth, and the incisors are used for cutting. Behind the incisors are the teeth used to tear or rip food. These are called the canine teeth. Canine teeth are usually more pointed than the other teeth. The flatter teeth in the rear of the mouth are called premolars and molars; the premolars and molars are used for mashing and grinding.

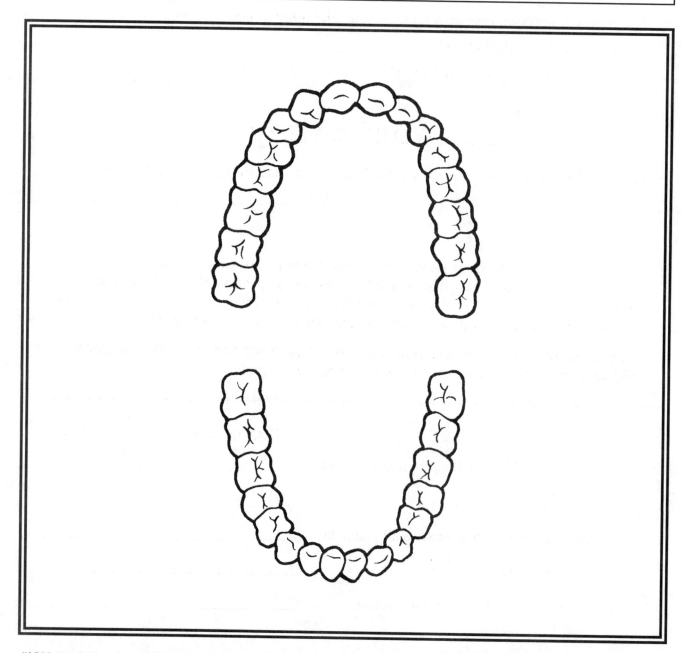

Sentence Comprehension

Directions: Read the following sentence carefully and answer the questions below "True" (T) or "False" (F).

> Fisk and Holland watched in awe as Koorina, a duck-billed platypus, chowed down on huge quantities of worms, bugs, and crayfish, apparently preparing to nurse her young.

1. Fisk and Holland watched Koorina nurse her young. _____

2. Koorina collected worms, bugs, and crayfish to feed her babies. _____

3. Koorina ate significantly more food in preparation for her young. _____

4. Koorina is a duck-billed platypus. _____

5. Koorina became overweight and was placed on a worm-only diet. _____

Word Study

Directions: For each sentence below, write the helping verb and/or action verb in the correct spaces.

> **Had**
>
> The word *had* is a **helping verb** that means "having something." Although a helping verb can be the main verb in a sentence, many helping verbs also "help" **action verbs**. For example, "The duck-billed platypus was eating more food than usual." In this sentence, the helping verb *was* actually helps the action verb *eating*.
>
> Helping verbs include: *is, am, are, was, were, has, have, had, be, been, do, does, did, can, will, shall, could, would, should, may, might, must.*

	Helping verb	**Action verb**
1. The scientists could watch the platypus in her pen.	_____	_____
2. Koorina is a duck-billed platypus.	_____	_____
3. I may be reading about platypuses until midnight!	_____	_____
4. Will you hand me the material?	_____	_____
5. The platypus hollowed a nest for her young.	_____	_____

Paragraph Comprehension

Directions: Read the paragraph below and answer the following questions.

The world did not get a look at the babies for six months. On April 3, they left the safety of the nesting burrow. Fisk, who has spent 10 years trying to breed captive platypuses, said that moment was "the biggest and best thing in my life!"

---

1. For six months,

    a. the world expressed disbelief that the babies existed.

    b. the platypus babies remained in their eggs.

    c. no one saw the platypus babies.

    d. Fisk tried to capture the mother platypus.

2. Fisk has spent ten years

    a. investigating platypus diet and eating habits.

    b. trying to breed wild platypuses.

    c. comparing the duck to the platypus.

    d. trying to breed captive platypuses.

3. Fisk said the moment was "the biggest and best thing in my life!" because

    a. he finally understood why the platypus had a duck-bill.

    b. he had never seen a live platypus.

    c. he had finally succeeded in breeding captive platypuses.

    d. he was ready to begin his next platypus experiment.

4. On April 3, the platypus babies

    a. left their nesting burrow.

    b. explored their environment.

    c. gained independence.

    d. all of the above

5. The author uses a direct quotation in the last sentence

    a. because he couldn't think of what to write.

    b. to use Fisk's exact words.

    c. because he felt sorry for Fisk.

    d. to let the reader share in Fisk's excitement.

    e. b and d

    f. all of the above

Whole Story Comprehension

Directions: Read the story below and answer the questions on the following page.

A Special Delivery

Something was definitely up at the platypus pen. Koorina, a female, and "N," a male, at Healesville Sanctuary near Melbourne, Australia, were spending quite a bit of time together. Then, on November 14, 1998, Koorina was seen gathering bunches of leaves from the surface of a small pond in the enclosure. She tucked them under her paddle-like tail and lugged them to a spot she had hollowed out under the roots of a tree. For five days she disappeared into her leaf-lined burrow.

The sanctuary's platypus experts, Norm Holland and Fisk (who uses only one name), could hardly contain their excitement. Could it be that Koorina was busy laying eggs? If so, she was only the second captive platypus ever to do so.

Over the next few weeks, a video camera trained on the platypus habitat allowed Fisk and Holland to observe the shy, duck-billed mammal without disturbing her. They watched in awe as Koorina chowed down on huge quantities of worms, bugs, and crayfish, apparently preparing to nurse her young. Soon she was eating 1 1/2 times her weight in food a day!

Then, by sometime in early December, Koorina made platypus history. Deep inside her burrow, two leathery grape-size eggs hatched. The tiny newborns each weighed less than a nickel. They had long lips that would later become beaks.

The world did not get a look at the babies for six months. On April 3, they left the safety of the nesting burrow. Fisk, who has spent 10 years trying to breed captive platypuses, said that moment was "the biggest and best thing in my life!"

The last time a platypus was born in captivity was during World War II. Corrie, born at Healesville in 1944, made the front-page news around the world. Though later attempts to breed the egg-laying mammals failed, Fisk believed he would succeed this time. The animals, he said, were "comfortable with their enclosure; the weather conditions were perfect." Perhaps most important of all, platypus love had bloomed: "Basically, 'N' and Koorina like each other."

One of the babies was put on display at the sanctuary in April, 1999.

Whole Story Comprehension *(cont.)*

Directions: After you have read the story on the previous page, answer the questions below.

1. At Healesville Sanctuary, prior to November 14, 1998, Koorina spent a lot of time

    a. exercising.

    b. with "N," a male platypus.

    c. getting to know the scientists.

    d. all of the above

2. Koorina prepared her nest by doing all of the following except

    a. gathering leaves.

    b. sorting leaves by color.

    c. eating more than normal.

    d. bringing leaves to her burrow.

3. Norm Holland and Fisk are

    a. the names of two platypuses.

    b. platypus experts.

    c. Australian poachers.

    d. veterinarians.

4. Hatching time for a platypus is

    a. one month.

    b. six months.

    c. nine months.

    d. one year.

5. The first time a platypus was born in captivity was

    a. during World War I.

    b. during the month of December.

    c. during World War II.

    d. in December, 1998.

6. Platypus eggs are

    a. grape-size.

    b. the texture of leather.

    c. yellow.

    d. a and b

    e. all of the above

7. At birth, platypus newborns

    a. look like a duck.

    b. eat $1\frac{1}{2}$ times their weight.

    c. are the weight of a nickel.

    d. quack.

8. Fisk believed he would succeed breeding "N" and Koorina for all of the following reasons except

    a. they were comfortable with their pen.

    b. the weather conditions were ideal.

    c. the two platypuses were in love.

    d. the new perfume Koorina wore.

Enrichment

Directions: Read the platypus facts below and answer the questions that follow.

Platypuses and echidnas (spiny anteaters), the only two mammals that hatch from eggs, are called *monotremes*.

Male platypuses have poison spurs on their hind legs, which they use to battle for mates. Their poison can cause humans pain.

When platypuses were first described in 1797, even scientists had a hard time believing such an odd creature could exist.

Once hunted in Australia for their thick, soft fur, platypuses are now protected by law.

---

1. An echidna is also known as a(n)

   a. insect that eats ants.
   b. spiny anteater.
   c. animals that eat insects.
   d. the place anteaters live.

2. What are the two mammals that hatch from eggs?

   a. platypus and people
   b. platypus and kangaroos
   c. platypus and echidnas
   d. There are not two mammals that hatch from eggs.

3. Male platypuses are different from female platypuses because

   a. they have spurs on their hind legs.
   b. they like to kick-box.
   c. they quack like a duck.
   d. their bills are longer.

Graphic Development

Directions: Create a time line highlighting the important events of the story "A Special Delivery." Then, write five questions that you might ask someone based on the information from the time line.

| |

1. _____

_____

2. _____

_____

3. _____

_____

4. _____

_____

5. _____

_____

Sentence Comprehension

Directions: Read the following sentence carefully and answer the questions below "True" (T) or "False" (F).

Many endangered tongues face another threat: young people who have no interest in speaking the language of their ancestors.

---

1. An "endangered tongue" means a language that is on the verge of extinction. _____

2. Young people want to speak the language everyone else speaks. _____

3. When young people attempt to learn their native language, their ancestors refuse to teach them. _____

4. An ancestor is an older relative. _____

5. One threat to various languages is young people. _____

Word Study

Directions: Look at the list of words below. Circle the words that are synonyms, words that mean the same thing, as the word *ancestor*. You may need to use the dictionary.

Ancestor

An ancestor is someone from whom one is descended. Our ancestors include relatives such as aunts, uncles, mother, father, and grandparents.

---

antecedent	ant	epilogue
ascendant	forebear	descendant
forefather	progenitor	generation

Paragraph Comprehension

Directions: Read the paragraph below and answer the following questions.

> When you hear the words *endangered* or *extinct*, you may think of rhinos, tigers, and other wildlife. But languages can also become endangered and extinct. Linguists, people who study languages, say about half the world's 6,500 languages are in trouble. Some have fewer than five living speakers, and nearly 3,000 may disappear in the next 100 years.

1. *Endangered* and *extinct*

   a. are synonyms.

   b. are antonyms.

   c. mean not protected or nonexistent.

   d. mean something awful is about to happen.

2. The languages that have fewer than five living speakers should

   a. have someone teach the language to other people.

   b. have someone write down their language to preserve it.

   c. accept the fact that the language will be lost forever.

   d. both a and b

3. A *linguist* is

   a. a person who knows how to speak "Ling."

   b. a person who knows all of the 6,500 world languages.

   c. a person who studies languages.

   d. a noodle dish originating in Italy.

4. Over the next 100 years, linguists believe

   a. 3,000 languages may disappear.

   b. English will be the only language spoken in the world.

   c. much wildlife will be extinct.

   d. people will rely on dictionaries.

5. Linguists believe _____ languages are in trouble.

   a. 6,500

   b. 100

   c. 3,250

   d. 3,000

Whole Story Comprehension

Directions: Read the story below and answer the questions on the following page.

Troubled Tongues

LeRoy Sealy's first day of first grade was probably the loneliest day of his life. He couldn't speak to any of the kids in his class and he couldn't understand a thing they were saying. "I was pretty much alone because I couldn't communicate," says Sealy, a Choctaw Native American. "I didn't learn English until starting school." Sealy knew only the Choctaw language, and no one in his class could speak it.

Sealy is now 33, and a professor of Choctaw at the University of Oklahoma in Norman. He still speaks Choctaw, as do about 12,000 people, but he is worried about the future of his native language. Choctaw is on the endangered-language list.

When you hear the words *endangered* or *extinct*, you may think of rhinos, tigers, and other wildlife. But languages can also become endangered and extinct. Linguists, people who study languages, say about half the world's 6,500 languages are in trouble. Some have fewer than five living speakers, and nearly 3,000 may disappear in the next 100 years.

Concerned linguists are working to save endangered languages. One group doing this work is the Endangered Language Fund (E.L.F.), which just awarded $10,000 for 10 language-preservation projects. The money will be used to make recordings of languages such as Maliseet, Juskokwim, Choctaw, and Klamath, so their words won't be lost forever.

How does a language become endangered? "The most common cause is probably that a small community comes into close contact with a larger one, and people begin using the dominant language," says linguist Doug Whalen, president of the E.L.F. Better technology and transportation have spread more common languages, including English, across the planet. Native languages are used less. In Australia, for instance, only about 10 speakers keep the Jingulu language alive. Most Australians speak English.

Sealy says governments have also hurt native languages. "Native American children sent to government schools in the 1950s and '60s were told not to speak their native languages either, believing that English would help them economically in life. This caused many languages to be lost."

Why should we care? "Every language has its way of expressing ideas about the world," explains Whalen. "When a language dies, we lose that insight."

Many endangered tongues face another threat: young people who have no interest in speaking the language of their ancestors. Sealy hopes young Native Americans will learn to value their cultural heritage and language.

"My niece, who's in fourth grade, is learning Choctaw, and although she mostly speaks English, she understands Choctaw when we speak with her," says Sealy. "We encourage her because the younger generations will be the ones to carry the language into the 21st century."

Whole Story Comprehension (cont.)

Directions: After you have read the story on the previous page, answer the questions below.

1. LeRoy Sealy's first day of first grade was lonely because
   a. he couldn't speak the language of the other children.
   b. he forgot his lunch.
   c. he had the flu.
   d. he did not know anyone.

2. In the third paragraph, the reader learns all of these facts except
   a. 6,500 languages in the world are in trouble.
   b. 3,000 languages may disappear in 100 years.
   c. statistics.
   d. Choctaw.

3. The author may have concluded with the anecdote about LeRoy Sealy's niece because
   a. there is hope for the Choctaw language, and pride for the culture.
   b. the niece is angry she cannot speak Choctaw.
   c. Sealy is jealous his niece speaks English so well.
   d. he is worried about the fate of the Choctaw language.

4. The author's purpose in the article is
   a. to let people know that languages can be endangered.
   b. to encourage people to learn Choctaw.
   c. to show how difficult it is to learn a new language.
   d. to explain why he forgot the Choctaw language.

5. A native language becomes endangered because
   a. a small community comes into close contact with a larger one, and the dominant language is used.
   b. people these days primarily speak English.
   c. books are only published in one language.
   d. foreign language is only offered at the high school level.

6. E.L.F
   a. is a group of elves who whisper languages into ears at night.
   b. stands for "Eat Less Food" so food will not become extinct.
   c. stands for "Endangered Language Fund" which works to save languages.
   d. is Doug Whalen's nickname.

7. Native Americans sent to government schools did not speak their native language for all of these reasons except:
   a. the schools told the students not to speak their native language.
   b. parents of these children didn't speak their native language at home.
   c. they had no way of writing their native language, only speaking it.
   d. the Native Americans were concerned with their children's future, and believed English would help them economically.
   e. both b and c

8. Choctaw is
   a. an African-American language.
   b. a Native-American language.
   c. a Native-American language that is now extinct.
   d. a type of wheat.

Enrichment

Directions: The chart below illustrates how to spell and say some common words and phrases in the Choctaw language. Choose one other language, besides English, and write the words that mean the same as the English expressions. Be sure to include a pronunciation guide. You may need to consult a dictionary for the language you choose.

Choctaw	English	Language: _____
halito (ha-li-to)	hello	
yakoke (yay-co-kee)	thank you	
Ikana (n-kah-na)	friend	
onahinli achukma (o-na-hin-lee a-chuk-ma)	good morning	
chi pisala hakinli (chee pee-sah-la ha-kin-lee)	I'll see you later	

Graphic Development

Directions: Fill in the family tree below. Research the language spoken by your relatives.

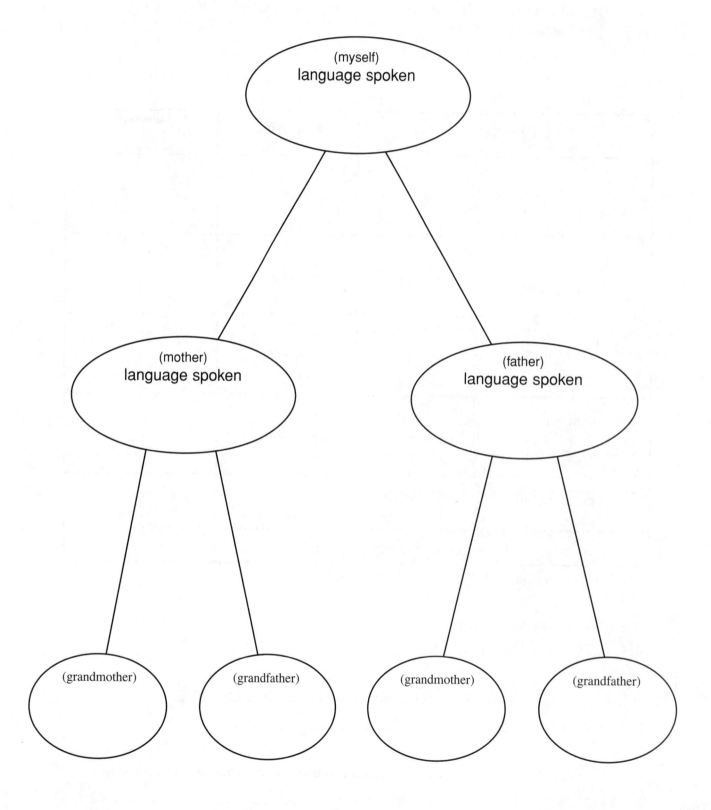

Sentence Comprehension

Directions: Read the following sentence carefully and answer the questions below "True" (T) or "False" (F).

On April 15, 1947, Jack Roosevelt Robinson broke the color barrier.

1. Jack Roosevelt Robinson died on April 15, 1947. _____

2. "Broke the color barrier" means that Robinson changed color. _____

3. A barrier is something that prohibits and restricts passage. _____

4. Jack Roosevelt Robinson was able to break through the color barrier. _____

5. After Robinson broke through the color barrier, he had to pay for it to be fixed. _____

Word Study

Directions: For the sentences below, determine whether the word *integrate* or *segregate* would be used to describe each situation.

Integrate
The word *integrate* means to join or unite all parts or groups.

Segregate
The opposite of integrate is *segregate*, which means to isolate.

1. This baseball season, there were no longer boys' teams and girls' teams. Because not enough coaches signed up, the teams included both boys and girls. _____

2. The school locker rooms were not unisex. There was a separate changing area for the boys, and a separate changing area for the girls. _____

3. Before the guest arrived at his surprise party, all of the guests remained in a closed-off room. _____

4. After I read my story, I wrote a new paragraph and used the cut-and-paste feature of my word processor so I didn't have to rewrite the whole story. _____

Paragraph Comprehension

Directions: Read the paragraph below and answer the following questions.

> Jackie Robinson went on to bat .297 and was named National League Rookie of the Year. For 10 years, he played outstanding baseball. His lifetime batting average: .311. On the bases, Robinson was dazzling; he stole 197 bases in his career. "Daring," he said, "that's half my game." In 1962, he became the first African-American player elected to the Baseball Hall of Fame.

1. In Jackie Robinson's rookie year, he

    a. batted 297 times.

    b. had a .297 batting average.

    c. had a .311 batting average.

    d. played for the American League.

2. Robinson credited 50% of his game to being

    a. African-American.

    b. gifted.

    c. daring.

    d. all of the above

3. Robinson was called "dazzling" because

    a. he had gleaming white teeth.

    b. he was the first African-American to play baseball.

    c. he had a great batting average.

    d. he was a fantastic base stealer.

4. In 1962,

    a. Robinson's baseball career began.

    b. he had a .311 batting average.

    c. he was elected to the Baseball Hall of Fame.

    d. Jackie Robinson stole 197 bases.

5. Jackie Robinson's career lasted

    a. 10 years.

    b. 15 years.

    c. 20 years.

    d. 25 years.

Whole Story Comprehension

Directions: Read the story below and answer the questions on the following page.

Thanks, Jackie!

Major league baseball's 1997 season opened with some shining moments from Seattle's Ken Griffey, Jr., Chicago's Albert Belle, and Cincinnati's Deion Sanders. Imagine opening day without those great players. Tough, isn't it? But 50 years ago, African-Americans were not allowed to play in the major leagues.

On April 15, 1947, Jack Roosevelt Robinson broke the color barrier. Wearing number 24, he stepped up to the plate for the Brooklyn Dodgers. Robinson did not get a hit that day, but through his courage, he forever changed the way Americans viewed baseball—and one another.

Jackie Robinson went on to bat .297 and was named National League Rookie of the Year. For 10 years, he played outstanding baseball. His lifetime batting average: .311. On the bases, Robinson was dazzling; he stole 197 bases in his career. "Daring," he said, "that's half my game." In 1962, he became the first African-American player elected to the Baseball Hall of Fame.

What makes Robinson's achievements more remarkable is that he performed so gracefully under so much pressure. Robinson received hate mail and even death threats. Spiteful pitchers aimed at his head, and base runners tried to spike him with their shoes.

At the time, America was a land of cruel racial divisions. In parts of the country, blacks and whites drank at separate water fountains and went to separate schools. Some hotels and restaurants refused to serve blacks.

In 1946, 15 of the 16 major league team owners voted against integration. Only Branch Rickey, the president of the Dodgers, believed blacks should play alongside whites.

Rickey signed Robinson to play for the Montreal Royals, a Dodger minor league team in 1945. He made Robinson promise that for his first two years in the majors he would not respond in anger when insulted. "Mr. Rickey, do you want a ballplayer who's afraid to fight back?" Robinson asked. "I want a player with guts," said Rickey, "The guts not to fight back."

It was a tough promise to keep. Fans threw garbage at Robinson. Opposing players hurled insults at him. One time in Cincinnati, Ohio, the abuse got so bad that shortstop PeeWee Reese called time out. He walked over to where Robinson was playing and put his arm around his teammate's shoulders. Years later, a sportswriter called Reese's display of friendship "baseball's finest moment."

The baseball season of 1997 was dedicated to Robinson. Players and umpires wore special patches bearing his name. President Bill Clinton took part in a ceremony honoring Robinson when the Los Angeles Dodgers played the New York Mets at Shea Stadium in New York City on April 15.

White Sox outfielder, Albert Belle, believes all players should be grateful for Robinson's tremendous courage battling bigotry. "I probably couldn't have dealt with it," said Belle. "It takes a big man to be the first in anything."

Whole Story Comprehension (cont.)

Directions: After you have read the story on the previous page, answer the questions below.

1. The author begins the story with examples of recent memorable moments in baseball because

    a. the athletes he names are all African-Americans.

    b. he is related to the athletes he names.

    c. he doesn't want to confuse the reader with basketball or football stars.

    d. none of the above

2. The first Major League team Jackie Robinson played for was the

    a. Brooklyn Dodgers.

    b. New York Mets.

    c. New York Yankees.

    d. Cincinnati White Sox.

3. White Sox outfielder Albert Belle believes all baseball players should

    a. get Jackie Robinson on their team.

    b. study Robinson's base-stealing techniques.

    c. be grateful for Robinson's courage battling bigotry.

    d. be in perfect physical condition.

4. Branch Rickey wanted a player with the "guts" to do what?

    a. fight when insulted

    b. not to fight back when provoked

    c. swing at all fast balls

    d. not wear a batting helmet

5. What does one sportswriter believe is "baseball's finest moment"?

    a. when President Clinton honored Jackie Robinson

    b. when Jackie Robinson became the first African-American to play major league baseball

    c. when PeeWee Reese put an arm around his teammate's shoulders

    d. when segregation on the baseball diamond ended

6. In 1946, how many major league team owners voted against integration?

    a. 10 out of 16

    b. all 16 owners

    c. 15 out of 16

    d. none

7. Robinson received the following cruel treatment during his baseball career except

    a. hate mail.

    b. death threats.

    c. insults from opposing players.

    d. food restrictions from Branch Rickey.

8. The ceremony honoring Jackie Robinson was held

    a. at Shea Stadium.

    b. in Los Angeles.

    c. on the fifty-year anniversary of Robinson's career.

    d. both a and c

    e. both b and c

Enrichment

Directions: Rewrite the sentences below using an apostrophe to not only show possession, but also to tighten the sentence.

Apostrophes

An apostrophe (') often denotes possession or belonging.

Consider the following sentence.

What makes Robinson's achievements more remarkable is that he performed so gracefully under so much pressure.

Using the apostrophe, the reader knows the achievements belong to Jackie Robinson. The possessive apostrophe also enables the writer to tighten the structure of the sentence, so that it does not read, "What makes the achievements of Robinson more remarkable is that he performed so gracefully under so much pressure."

---

1. Ken Griffey, Jr., who plays for the Seattle Mariners, is an outfielder.

   _____

   _____

2. The bat that belonged to Jackie Robinson is in the Baseball Hall of Fame.

   _____

   _____

3. The finest moment that belongs to baseball was when Pee Wee Reese put his arm around the shoulders of his teammate Jackie Robinson.

   _____

   _____

Graphic Development

Directions: Design a trophy symbolizing Jackie Roosevelt Robinson's achievement as the first African-American baseball player.

Sentence Comprehension

Directions: Read the following sentence carefully and answer the questions below "True" (T) or "False" (F).

In 1997, kids spent $750 million on soda, candy, and chips in school vending machines!

1. The sentence ends with an exclamation point because of the amount of money kids spend on vending machines. _____

2. Kids spent 750 million on grocery store junk food. _____

3. School vending machines make millions of dollars. _____

4. In 1998, the amount spent by kids on soda, candy, and chips doubled. _____

5. Another way to write $750 million is $750,000,000. _____

Word Study

Directions: The $ is the universal symbol for money. When the $ is before numbers, the numbers equal the amount of money. Therefore, $2.70 is another way of saying two dollars and seventy cents.

Write the correct dollar amount in word form for each amount below.

1. $5.89 _____

2. $143.50 _____

3. $2,500,275 _____

Write the correct dollar amount for each of the following.

4. four-hundred twenty-thousand dollars _____

5. six dollars and sixty-seven cents _____

6. five million three hundred thousand dollars and forty-two cents _____

Paragraph Comprehension

Directions: Read the paragraph below and answer the following questions.

"Soda pop is junk," declares nutritionist Michael Jacobson. "It has no vitamins, no minerals, no protein, and no fiber." Jacobson is the director of the Center for Science in the Public Interest and the author of "Liquid Candy," a 1998 report on the health effects of soft drinks. Heaping helpings of sugar from soft drinks can lead to many health problems, including obesity and tooth decay.

1. "Liquid Candy" is

    a. a book about how candy is made.

    b. a book about soda.

    c. a report on how soda affects health.

    d. a new drinkable candy available in lime, cherry, and grape.

2. "Soda pop is junk,"

    a. are lyrics in a popular song.

    b. according to nutritionist Michael Jacobson.

    c. because of the type of aluminum used in cans.

    d. because most soda ends up going down drainpipes.

3. Heaping helpings of sugar may lead to

    a. many health problems.

    b. obesity.

    c. tooth decay.

    d. all of the above

4. The best synonym for *obesity* is

    a. skinny.

    b. fat.

    c. grossly overweight.

    d. physically fit.

5. Soda is considered "junk" because

    a. people litter.

    b. soda has no nutritional value.

    c. soda makes people burp.

    d. soda is fizzy.

Whole Story Comprehension

Directions: Read the story below and answer the questions on the following page.

A Sweet Deal

Bridget Hickson, 13, starts each school day with a pop—the sugary, fizzy kind. The seventh-grader in New York City drinks one 20-ounce bottle of Coke or Sprite before classes begin at 8 A.M. At lunchtime, she guzzles two more bottles of soda pop. "I like the way it tickles my throat," she says. Total cost for the three bottles of bubbly pop: $2.70. Total teaspoonfuls of sugar in the three bottles: about 50.

Bridget's passion for pop is not that unusual. Kids today are drinking more soda than ever before, and many are buying it in school. In 1997, kids spent $750 million on soda, candy, and chips in school vending machines!

While soda companies get much of that money, schools keep some, too. Money from soda-machine sales helps pay for books, computers, sports programs, and after-school activities. School officials say they cannot afford to lose those funds.

But health experts are concerned that selling sugary soda in schools encourages poor nutrition. They point out that a 12-ounce can of soda contains 10 teaspoonfuls of sugar and has no vitamins or protein. They want schools to unplug their soda machines.

In Florida, the school soda-machine debate has recently exploded like a shaken-up can of you-know-what. In March, 1999, Florida's Governor Jeb Bush asked the department of education to make it easier for high school kids to buy soft drinks. Bush supports soda sales because they sweeten school budgets.

Since 1997, students in Florida have not been allowed to use school soft-drink machines until one hour after lunch. The rule is intended to encourage kids to buy milk and other healthy drinks at lunchtime. But as a result, schools in Florida are collecting fewer dollars from soda sales. John Fox, the athletic director in Duvall County, Florida, says sports programs in his county have lost $450,000 since the vending-machine restrictions began two years ago. That money was supposed to fund "everything from transportation to new uniforms," says Fox. For now, new uniforms will have to wait.

"Soda pop is junk," declares nutritionist Michael Jacobson. "It has no vitamins, no minerals, no protein, and no fiber." Jacobson is the director of the Center for Science in the Public Interest and the author of "Liquid Candy," a 1998 report on the health effects of soft drinks. Heaping helpings of sugar from soft drinks can lead to many health problems, including obesity and tooth decay.

In addition, kids who fill up on soda instead of more nutritious foods miss out on important vitamins and minerals. Choosing soda over milk, for example, prevents some kids from getting the calcium they need to build strong bones and teeth.

What do you think? Are soda machines in schools a good idea or too much of a threat to kids' health?

Whole Story Comprehension (cont.)

Directions: After you have read the story on the previous page, answer the questions below.

1. Schools use money from soda-machines sales for all of the following except

    a. nutrition counseling.

    b. computers.

    c. sports equipment.

    d. after-school activities.

2. Health experts are concerned that selling soda in schools

    a. encourages poor nutrition.

    b. makes kids learn less.

    c. makes kids too active.

    d. doesn't teach the value of money.

3. A 12-ounce can of soda contains how much sugar?

    a. 10 tablespoons

    b. 10 teaspoons

    c. 100 tablespoons

    d. 1 teaspoon

4. Governor Jeb Bush supports soda sales in schools in

    a. March.

    b. New York City.

    c. Florida.

    d. the United States.

5. Sports programs in Duvall County have lost how much money since vending-machine restrictions?

    a. $45,000

    b. $4,500

    c. $450,000

    d. $4,500,000

6. The most important reason for kids to drink milk is

    a. the calcium milk provides.

    b. for strong bones.

    c. for strong teeth.

    d. all of the above

7. The author's opinion on the soda issue is

    a. soda vending machines should be allowed in schools.

    b. soda vending machines should not be allowed in schools.

    c. both sides are presented equally.

    d. not to re-elect Jeb Bush as governor.

8. The author ends "A Sweet Deal" with a question because

    a. the author enjoys soda.

    b. the author lives in Florida.

    c. the author wants the readers to debate the issue.

    d. the author wants readers to take daily vitamins.

136

Enrichment

Directions: Based on the graph, answer the following questions.

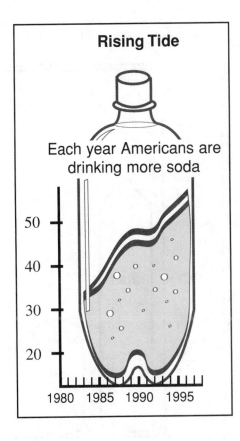

Rising Tide

Each year Americans are drinking more soda

1. How many gallons of soda did an average person drink in 1991?

   _____

2. The amount of soda each person drinks is

   a. increasing annually.

   b. decreasing annually.

   c. staying the same.

   d. not clear.

3. In 1980, the amount of soda the average person drank in a year was how many gallons? _____

4. In your opinion, why is soda consumption increasing? _____

   _____

   _____

   _____

5. In your opinion, what are the health effects of this increase in soda consumption? _____

   _____

   _____

   _____

   _____

Graphic Development

Directions: Based on the graph, answer the following questions.

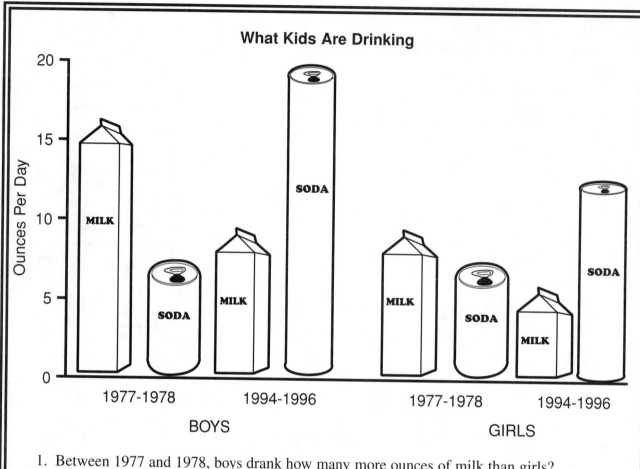

1. Between 1977 and 1978, boys drank how many more ounces of milk than girls?

   _____

2. Based on the graph, what gender enjoys soda more?

   _____

3. How many more ounces of soda did boys drink between 1994-1996 compared with 1977-1978?

   _____

4. Milk consumption is declining in both boys and girls because of what reasons, in your opinion?

   _____

Answer Key

Lesson 1
Page 19
Sentence Comprehension

1. T
2. F
3. T
4. F
5. F

Word Study

1. coyotes
2. foxes
3. badgers
4. eagles
5. bears
6. persons/people
7. moose
8. rodents
9. mice
10. puppies

Page 20
Paragraph Comprehension

1. d
2. b
3. b
4. a
5. d

Page 22
Whole Story Comprehension

1. e
2. e
3. b
4. c
5. d
6. d
7. a
8. d

Page 23
Enrichment

At Yellowstone National Park, wolves are now endangered. The Supreme Court of the United States may hold the wolves' existence in their hands. A group of ranchers want the American Gray Wolf returned to Canada, but the National Wildlife Federation believes the wolves maintain Yellowstone's ecosystem and symbolize the American West. Should the wolves be allowed to remain? The courts will decide.

Lesson 2
Page 25
Sentence Comprehension

1. T
2. F
3. T
4. T
5. F

Word Study

1. illegally
2. angrily
3. happily
4. diligently
5. fortunately

Page 26
Paragraph Comprehension

1. b
2. b
3. a
4. c
5. a

Page 28
Whole Story Comprehension

1. d
2. d
3. d
4. b
5. b
6. d
7. c
8. c

Lesson 3
Page 31
Sentence Comprehension

1. F
2. T
3. T
4. F
5. T

Word Study

1. 2
2. 4
3. 3
4. 1

Page 32
Paragraph Comprehension

1. d
2. d
3. a
4. b
5. d

Page 34
Whole Story Comprehension

1. c
2. a
3. d
4. d
5. b
6. c
7. d
8. b

Page 35
Enrichment

1. At West Point, Henry O. Flipper endured many hardships: insults, ostracism, and loneliness.
2. Henry O. Flipper taught fellow African-Americans and cadets a great lesson: perseverance will achieve greater results than anger.
3. President Clinton gave Flipper a full pardon: "This good man has now completely recovered his good name. Although the wheels of justice turn slowly at times, still they turn."

Page 36
Graphic Development

1. 1856
2. 1873
3. 1877
4. 1881
5. 1882
6. 1940
7. 1976
8. 1999

Lesson 4
Page 37
Sentence Comprehension

1. F
2. T
3. T
4. T
5. F

Word Study

1. *On the first morning*, we cleared the garbage from the vacant lot.
2. *By lunchtime*, we had filled 50 trash bags with junk.
3. *At the end of the first day*, the lot looked better!
4. *After about two weeks*, the plants began growing!
5. *Tonight*, I finally realized how beneficial the garden has been for our community.

Page 38
Paragraph Comprehension

1. b
2. c
3. a
4. c
5. b

Answer Key (cont.)

Page 40

Whole Story Comprehension

1. b
2. d
3. d
4. c
5. d
6. d
7. d
8. a

Page 41

1. us
2. me
3. us
4. me
5. We
6. I

Page 42

Graphic Development

Comic strips will vary. Assess for creativity and correct sequence.

Lesson 5

Page 43

Sentence Comprehension

1. F
2. F
3. T
4. F
5. F

Word Study

1. c
2. b
3. a
4. a
5. c
6. b

Page 44

Paragraph Comprehension

1. c
2. b
3. a
4. a
5. d

Page 46

Whole Story Comprehension

1. a
2. b
3. c
4. a
5. c
6. b
7. d
8. b

Page 47

Enrichment

1. d
2. False
3. Gulf of Mexico, Caribbean Sea, Atlantic Ocean
4. Answers will vary.
5. Yes, although answers may vary.

Lesson 6

Page 49

Sentence Comprehension

1. T
2. T
3. F
4. T
5. T

Word Study

1. education
2. educational
3. educator
4. educable
5. educate
6. educationally

Page 50

Paragraph Comprehension

1. c
2. d
3. d
4. a
5. d

Page 52

Whole Story Comprehension

1. c
2. d
3. d
4. b
5. c
6. b
7. d
8. d

Page 53

Enrichment

Paragraphs will vary. Assess on whether the paragraph states a clear opinion in the topic sentence, proves and defends the position, and has a conclusion that summarizes the paragraph well.

Lesson 7

Page 55

Sentence Comprehension

1. F
2. F
3. T
4. F
5. F

Word Study

1. couldn't
2. I'd
3. We're
4. they've
5. He'll

Page 56

Paragraph Comprehension

1. d
2. b
3. b
4. b
5. d

Page 58

Whole Story Comprehension

1. c
2. d
3. d
4. d
5. d
6. d
7. b
8. a

Page 59

Enrichment

Possible action verbs for zebra are gallop, trot, run.

Answers will vary.

Lesson 8

Page 61

Sentence Comprehension

1. F
2. T
3. T
4. T
5. F

Word Study

1. secured, deep
2. colorless
3. poisonous
4. sulfuric, human
5. sparkling, head

Page 62

Paragraph Comprehension

1. d
2. c
3. d
4. c
5. c

Page 64

Whole Story Comprehension

1. d
2. c
3. b
4. b
5. c
6. a
7. c
8. e

Answer Key *(cont.)*

Page 65
Enrichment
Answers may vary.

Lesson 9

Page 67
Sentence Comprehension
1. T
2. F
3. F
4. F
5. T

Word Study
1. lead-led
2. has-had
3. know-knew
4. say-said/feel-felt
5. win-won

Page 68
Paragraph Comprehension
1. a
2. d
3. b
4. d
5. c

Page 70
Whole Story Comprehension
1. d
2. a
3. d
4. d
5. d
6. c
7. b
8. a

Page 71
Enrichment
1. flashback
2. no flashback
3. flashback/no flashback, could be
   argued either way
4. flashback
5. no flashback

Lesson 10

Page 73
Sentence Comprehension
1. T
2. F
3. F
4. F
5. T

Word Study
1. reserve
2. preserve
3. conservation
4. conserve
5. preservation
6. reservation

Page 74
Paragraph Comprehension
1. d
2. c
3. d
4. d
5. c

Page 76
Whole Story Comprehension
1. a
2. d
3. c
4. b
5. c
6. d
7. answers will vary
8. d

Page 77
Enrichment
1. simile
2. simile
3. metaphor
4. metaphor
5.–6. Sentences will vary.

Page 78
Graphic Development
Map of the Everglades ecosystem should
reflect information in the story.

Lesson 11

Page 79
Sentence Comprehension
1. F
2. F
3. F
4. T
5. T

Word Study
1. Noun
2. Noun
3. Verb
4. Verb

Page 80
Paragraph Comprehension
1. a
2. b
3. d
4. e
5. b

Page 82
Whole Story Comprehension
1. d
2. d
3. c
4. c
5. a
6. a
7. e
8. c

Page 83
Enrichment
1. pod
2. colony
3. swarm
4. bunch
5. school
6. gaggle

Page 84
Graphic Development
1. Lake Victoria
2. Lake Lagaja
3. 6: Ndabaka, Ruana, Togoro,
   Musabi, Dutwa, Ndoha

Lesson 12

Page 85
Sentence Comprehension
1. T
2. T
3. T
4. F
5. F

Word Study
1. noun
2. verb
3. noun
4. verb
5. noun

Page 86
Paragraph Comprehension
1. c
2. b
3. b
4. a
5. c

Page 88
Whole Story Comprehension
1. b
2. c
3. c
4. b
5. d
6. c
7. d
8. d
9. e

Page 89
Enrichment
1. lifeboats
2. shipwreck
3. gangplank
4. dogsleds
5. cannonball
6. offshore

Answer Key (cont.)

Page 90
Graphic Development

1. Atlantic Ocean and the Weddell Sea
2. South Georgia Island
3. The crew was no longer on the *Endurance*, but in lifeboats.
4. Elephant Island
5. 324 days(from December 7, 1914 through October 27, 1915)

Lesson 13
Page 91
Sentence Comprehension

1. F
2. F
3. T
4. F
5. T

Word Study

Carnivore

tiger

alligator

lion

T-rex

Herbivore

horse

caterpillar

koala

deer

Insectivore

frog

bat

lizard

snake

Page 92
Paragraph Comprehension

1. c
2. b
3. b
4. c
5. c

Page 94
Whole Story Comprehension

1. a
2. c
3. d
4. a
5. b
6. d
7. b
8. d

Page 95
Enrichment

1. strange-looking
2. full-time
3. well-educated
4. bright-eyed
5. meat-eating

Page 96
Graphic Development
Answers may vary.

Lesson 14
Page 97
Sentence Comprehension

1. F
2. T
3. F
4. T
5. F

Word Study

1. f
2. c
3. d
4. e
5. b
6. a

Page 98
Paragraph Comprehension

1. d
2. c
3. a
4. d
5. a

Page 100
Whole Story Comprehension

1. b
2. c
3. c
4. d
5. b
6. d
7. d
8. b

Page 101
Enrichment

1. as soon as possible/ASAP
2. students against drunk driving/SADD
3. sports utility vehicle/SUV
4. most valuable player/MVP
5. United Parcel Service/UPS

Lesson 15
Page 103
Sentence Comprehension

1. T
2. F
3. F
4. F
5. T

Word Study
Answers will vary.

1. Greenland is the largest island in the world.
2. Warriors and tradesmen explored Greenland.
3. Viking families lived in homes along narrow inlets that were called fjords.

Page 104
Paragraph Comprehension

1. c
2. a
3. c
4. c
5. a

Page 106
Whole Story Comprehension

1. c
2. a
3. b
4. b
5. c
6. d
7. d
8. c

Page 107
Enrichment

1. T
2. T
3. F
4. T
5. F

Lesson 16
Page 109
Sentence Comprehension

1. F
2. F
3. T
4. T
5. T

Word Study

1. its
2. It's
3. It's
4. its
5. it's

Page 110
Paragraph Comprehension

1. c
2. a
3. a
4. d
5. e

Answer Key (cont.)

Page 112

Whole Story Comprehension

1. a
2. c
3. b
4. a
5. a
6. d
7. a
8. d

Page 113

Enrichment

1. Get your toothbrush.
2. Squeeze a pea-sized amount of toothpaste onto the brush.
3. Moisten the toothbrush slightly.
4. Brush up and down, side to side, scrubbing and polishing each tooth for at least one minute.
5. Rinse your mouth with clean water, swirl water around mouth, and spit into sink.
6. Rinse toothbrush and allow to air dry.

Lesson 17

Page 115

Sentence Comprehension

1. F
2. F
3. T
4. T
5. F

Word Study

1. could/watch
2. is, no action verb
3. may be/reading
4. will/hand
5. hollowed (no helping verb)

Page 116

Paragraph Comprehension

1. c
2. d
3. c
4. a
5. e

Page 118

Whole Story Comprehension

1. b
2. b
3. b
4. a
5. c
6. d
7. c
8. d

Page 119

Enrichment

1. b
2. c
3. a

Lesson 18

Page 121

Sentence Comprehension

1. T
2. T
3. F
4. T
5. T

Word Study

antecedent

ascendant

descendant

forefather

progenitor

Page 122

Paragraph Comprehension

1. c
2. d
3. c
4. a
5. c

Page 124

Whole Story Comprehension

1. a
2. d
3. a
4. a
5. a
6. c
7. e
8. b

Lesson 19

Page 127

Sentence Comprehension

1. F
2. F
3. T
4. T
5. F

Word Study

1. integrate
2. segregate
3. segregate
4. integrate

Page 128

Paragraph Comprehension

1. b
2. c
3. d
4. c
5. a

Page 130

Whole Story Comprehension

1. a
2. a
3. c
4. b
5. c
6. c
7. d
8. d

Page 131

Enrichment

1. The Seattle Mariner's Ken Griffey, Jr. is an outfielder.
2. Jackie Robinson's bat is in the Baseball Hall of Fame.
3. Baseball's finest moment was when Pee Wee Reese put his arm around his teammate's shoulders.

Lesson 20

Page 133

Sentence Comprehension

1. T
2. F
3. T
4. F
5. T

Word Study

1. five dollars and eighty nine cents
2. one hundred forty-three dollars and fifty cents
3. two million five hundred thousand two hundred seventy-five dollars
4. $420,000
5. $6.67
6. $5,300,000.42

Page 134

Paragraph Comprehension

1. c
2. b
3. d
4. c
5. b

Page 136

Whole Story Comprehension

1. a
2. a
3. b
4. c
5. c
6. d
7. b
8. c

Page 137

Enrichment

Rising tide

1. approximately 48 gallons
2. a-increasing annually
3. 35 gallons
4.–5. answers will vary

Page 138

Graphic Development

What Kids Are Drinking

1. 5 ounces more
2. boys
3. 5 ounces
4. Answers will vary.`

Answer Sheet

Directions: Fill in the bubble of the correct answer "a," "b," "c," "d," or "e" on this sheet. If the answer is "True," fill in the "a" bubble, and if the answer is "False," fill in the "b" bubble.

T F   T F   T F   T F

___ (a) (b) (c) (d) (e)   ___ (a) (b) (c) (d) (e)   ___ (a) (b) (c) (d) (e)   ___ (a) (b) (c) (d) (e)
___ (a) (b) (c) (d) (e)   ___ (a) (b) (c) (d) (e)   ___ (a) (b) (c) (d) (e)   ___ (a) (b) (c) (d) (e)
___ (a) (b) (c) (d) (e)   ___ (a) (b) (c) (d) (e)   ___ (a) (b) (c) (d) (e)   ___ (a) (b) (c) (d) (e)
___ (a) (b) (c) (d) (e)   ___ (a) (b) (c) (d) (e)   ___ (a) (b) (c) (d) (e)   ___ (a) (b) (c) (d) (e)
___ (a) (b) (c) (d) (e)   ___ (a) (b) (c) (d) (e)   ___ (a) (b) (c) (d) (e)   ___ (a) (b) (c) (d) (e)
___ (a) (b) (c) (d) (e)   ___ (a) (b) (c) (d) (e)   ___ (a) (b) (c) (d) (e)   ___ (a) (b) (c) (d) (e)
___ (a) (b) (c) (d) (e)   ___ (a) (b) (c) (d) (e)   ___ (a) (b) (c) (d) (e)   ___ (a) (b) (c) (d) (e)
___ (a) (b) (c) (d) (e)   ___ (a) (b) (c) (d) (e)   ___ (a) (b) (c) (d) (e)   ___ (a) (b) (c) (d) (e)
___ (a) (b) (c) (d) (e)   ___ (a) (b) (c) (d) (e)   ___ (a) (b) (c) (d) (e)   ___ (a) (b) (c) (d) (e)
___ (a) (b) (c) (d) (e)   ___ (a) (b) (c) (d) (e)   ___ (a) (b) (c) (d) (e)   ___ (a) (b) (c) (d) (e)
___ (a) (b) (c) (d) (e)   ___ (a) (b) (c) (d) (e)   ___ (a) (b) (c) (d) (e)   ___ (a) (b) (c) (d) (e)
___ (a) (b) (c) (d) (e)   ___ (a) (b) (c) (d) (e)   ___ (a) (b) (c) (d) (e)   ___ (a) (b) (c) (d) (e)
___ (a) (b) (c) (d) (e)   ___ (a) (b) (c) (d) (e)   ___ (a) (b) (c) (d) (e)   ___ (a) (b) (c) (d) (e)
___ (a) (b) (c) (d) (e)   ___ (a) (b) (c) (d) (e)   ___ (a) (b) (c) (d) (e)   ___ (a) (b) (c) (d) (e)
___ (a) (b) (c) (d) (e)   ___ (a) (b) (c) (d) (e)   ___ (a) (b) (c) (d) (e)   ___ (a) (b) (c) (d) (e)
___ (a) (b) (c) (d) (e)   ___ (a) (b) (c) (d) (e)   ___ (a) (b) (c) (d) (e)   ___ (a) (b) (c) (d) (e)
___ (a) (b) (c) (d) (e)   ___ (a) (b) (c) (d) (e)   ___ (a) (b) (c) (d) (e)   ___ (a) (b) (c) (d) (e)
___ (a) (b) (c) (d) (e)   ___ (a) (b) (c) (d) (e)   ___ (a) (b) (c) (d) (e)   ___ (a) (b) (c) (d) (e)
___ (a) (b) (c) (d) (e)   ___ (a) (b) (c) (d) (e)   ___ (a) (b) (c) (d) (e)   ___ (a) (b) (c) (d) (e)
___ (a) (b) (c) (d) (e)   ___ (a) (b) (c) (d) (e)   ___ (a) (b) (c) (d) (e)   ___ (a) (b) (c) (d) (e)
___ (a) (b) (c) (d) (e)   ___ (a) (b) (c) (d) (e)   ___ (a) (b) (c) (d) (e)   ___ (a) (b) (c) (d) (e)
___ (a) (b) (c) (d) (e)   ___ (a) (b) (c) (d) (e)   ___ (a) (b) (c) (d) (e)   ___ (a) (b) (c) (d) (e)
___ (a) (b) (c) (d) (e)   ___ (a) (b) (c) (d) (e)   ___ (a) (b) (c) (d) (e)   ___ (a) (b) (c) (d) (e)
___ (a) (b) (c) (d) (e)   ___ (a) (b) (c) (d) (e)   ___ (a) (b) (c) (d) (e)   ___ (a) (b) (c) (d) (e)
___ (a) (b) (c) (d) (e)   ___ (a) (b) (c) (d) (e)   ___ (a) (b) (c) (d) (e)   ___ (a) (b) (c) (d) (e)
___ (a) (b) (c) (d) (e)   ___ (a) (b) (c) (d) (e)   ___ (a) (b) (c) (d) (e)   ___ (a) (b) (c) (d) (e)
___ (a) (b) (c) (d) (e)   ___ (a) (b) (c) (d) (e)   ___ (a) (b) (c) (d) (e)   ___ (a) (b) (c) (d) (e)
___ (a) (b) (c) (d) (e)   ___ (a) (b) (c) (d) (e)   ___ (a) (b) (c) (d) (e)   ___ (a) (b) (c) (d) (e)
___ (a) (b) (c) (d) (e)   ___ (a) (b) (c) (d) (e)   ___ (a) (b) (c) (d) (e)   ___ (a) (b) (c) (d) (e)
___ (a) (b) (c) (d) (e)   ___ (a) (b) (c) (d) (e)   ___ (a) (b) (c) (d) (e)   ___ (a) (b) (c) (d) (e)
___ (a) (b) (c) (d) (e)   ___ (a) (b) (c) (d) (e)   ___ (a) (b) (c) (d) (e)   ___ (a) (b) (c) (d) (e)
___ (a) (b) (c) (d) (e)   ___ (a) (b) (c) (d) (e)   ___ (a) (b) (c) (d) (e)   ___ (a) (b) (c) (d) (e)
___ (a) (b) (c) (d) (e)   ___ (a) (b) (c) (d) (e)   ___ (a) (b) (c) (d) (e)   ___ (a) (b) (c) (d) (e)
___ (a) (b) (c) (d) (e)   ___ (a) (b) (c) (d) (e)   ___ (a) (b) (c) (d) (e)   ___ (a) (b) (c) (d) (e)